KI

Energy for Everybody

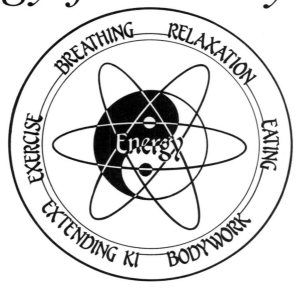

By Louise Taylor and Betty Bryant

Japan Publications, Inc.

Note to the reader: The information contained in this book is not intended to be used in the diagnosis, prescription, or treatment of disease or any health disorder whatsoever. Nor is this information intended to replace competent medical care. This book is a compendium of information which may be used as an adjunct to a rational and responsible health care plan.

Published by JAPAN PUBLICATIONS, INC., Tokyo and New York

Distributors:
UNITED STATES: *Kodansha International/USA, Ltd., through Farrar, Straus & Giroux, 19 Union Square West, New York, 10003.* CANADA: *Fitzhenry & Whiteside Ltd., 195 Allstate Parkway, Markham, Ontario, L3R 4T8.* BRITISH ISLES: *Premier Book Marketing Ltd., 1 Gower Street, London WC1E 6HA.* EUROPEAN CONTINENT: *European Book Service PBD, Strijkviertel 63, 3454 PK De Meern, The Netherlands.* AUSTRALIA AND NEW ZEALAND: *Bookwise International, 54 Crittenden Road, Findon, South Australia 5007.* THE FAR EAST AND JAPAN: *Japan Publications Trading Co., Ltd., 1-2-1, Sarugaku-cho, Chiyoda-ku, Tokyo 101.*

First edition: May 1990

ISBN 0-87040-786-4

Printed in U.S.A.

Preface

The aim of this book is to stimulate the reader's interest in a new way of learning about and working with many different techniques that, for many, have brought about increased energy and stamina. After looking through the offerings in the health and fitness sections of countless bookstores, we concluded that there was a need for a book that explains the body's energy systems in a readily understandable way and offeres interesting and useful insights concerning this fascinating subject.

Our research for the book led us to a discovery of the Eastern concepts of health and well-being. We found that a central theme in the Eastern philosophies is the recognition of a vital force or life energy that flows throughout each human being. It follows a predictable pathway that includes every part of the body. This "lifeforce" and its many functions is the central theme of the book. It has been given many names and has been recognized by many cultures throughout the world. In Japan it is called *Ki*.

Most of us take our energy levels for granted and work and play within limitations that we perceive as normal for us. By referring often to *Ki: Energy for Everybody*, you will soon begin to understand your own energy needs and requirements. You will easily learn to apply many new skills that raise low energy levels, eliminate fatigue, and enable you to maintain a high degree of vibrant and abundant energy each and every day.

When you have a thorough understanding of your energy systems and discover for yourself how you increase or deplete your energy, you may then choose from among the many methods presented in this book for gaining and keeping an abundance of stamina. You will be able to rediscover the integration of mind, body and spirit that you felt as a child and also experience the joy and freedom that accompany a consistently high level of vitality. Most of all, you will learn simple steps to follow that will invite you to rediscover your unlimited energy potential.

Throughout your life you have undoubtedly experienced variations in your energy levels. On mornings when you arise feeling out of sorts your energy is depressed and heavy. It takes an extra effort to get going and the people and events around you are viewed with a measure of lethargy and indifference. Other mornings you arise feeling excited about a project you are planning or about the people you are going to be with. You feel light and ready for the day, eager to start. What makes the difference between these two alternate states of being? In *Ki: Energy for Everybody* you will find the answer. Admittedly, these are extreme examples and most of us maintain energy levels that are somewhere in between. However, if you would like to wake up each day feeling abundantly alive, this book can be a constant guide and inspiration.

Ki: Energy for Everbody is easy to follow and use. You are free to choose, for your interest, any of the chapters in any order, at any time. Chapter 1 will take you on a guided tour of your energy systems as you discover how you receive and process energy from your environment. In Chapter 2 you will learn how the food you eat converts into the power the cells of your body need to function properly and efficiently. From working with the exercises in Chapter 3 you will learn how the air you breathe and the manner in which you breathe it determines the amount of energy that you have at your disposal. Chapter 4 will give you a working knowledge of the importance of the proper amount and kinds of exercise that add increased stamina to your life. Chapter 5 will show you how to take charge of the tensions that block your vitality. Through easy-to-learn exercises you will find the secrets of many ancient civilizations that bring about a state of complete rest and relaxation. In Chapter 6 you will discover the importance of bodywork and how to choose the system that is just right for you. Chapter 7 will help you to rediscover lightheartedness and joyfulness by focusing on the playfulness and creativity that all of us share. By looking at resources for fun and pleasure you will be drawing upon a vital source of health and energy.

It is our hope that you will truly enjoy the time you spend with *Ki: Energy for Everybody*. As teachers in a community college we are both aware that there is a great difference between knowing about something and personally experiencing that knowledge. Therefore, our aim has been to present the contents of the book in a way that will enable you to benefit from spending just a few minutes practicing one of the exercises or by making an in-depth study of its contents.

In the following chapters you will find a wealth of information and new ideas. The techniques and knowledge that we have included are those that we have found to be of value personally. We also have enjoyed sharing them with many students in our various classes. Like them, you can now discover for yourself how you receive energy from your environment, transform it within you for your personal use, and then send it out to affect the world around you.

Acknowledgment

Our sincere and grateful thanks to Bill Bryant and Art Taylor for their contribution and support.

Our thanks also go to Donna Taylor for her invaluable assistance and to Dr. Oscar Janiger for the use of his extensive library.

Contents

List of Figures

12

List of Charts

Energy

Understanding Ki

For thousands of years the Eastern cultures have taught that the interaction between two opposing forces has created the constantly changing world in which we live. From their point of view, the entire universe is held in balance between the contraction of a negative force (*yin*) and the expansion of a positive force (*yang*). Within this belief system, which is still widely held today in China and Japan, the contraction and expansion of yin and yang is thought to be the source of the energy that animates all living things. Man's energy and universal energy are seen to be the same, as man surrounds a small portion of the energy of the universe with his body and says, "This is Me." This energy is called *Ki* in Japan, *Chi* in China and *Prana* in India. Within these cultures it is also taught that everything on earth can be divided into two different aspects. For example, the yin characteristics of cold, darkness, shade, and passiveness can be contrasted with the yang characteristics of heat, light, sunshine, and activity.

In the sixth century B.C. a Chinese philosopher, Lao Tzu wrote:

Being and non-being produce each other;
Difficult and easy complete each other;
Long and short contrast each other;
High and low distinguish each other;
Sound and voice harmonize each other;
Front and back follow each other."

Of utmost importance in Oriental philosophy is the establishment of a balance and harmony between yin and yang. For example, if yin (cold) is too weak then yang (hot) will be too strong. However, a comfortable balance is experienced when the temperature is neither too cold nor too hot.

Fig. 1   Yin and Yang

Since nature always tends toward balance, eventually everything becomes its opposite. This theory is illustrated by the traditional Chinese symbol of yin and yang showing the two parts divided into yin (black)—the character for yin originally meant the shady side of a slope—and yang (white). The small circles of opposite shading illustrate that a part of yin must remain yang and a part of yang must remain yin. The dynamic curve dividing them suggests that they are continuously merging. Thus, yin and yang create each other, transform into each other and depend upon each other for definition.

The interchange of these two forces is seen to bring about the seasonal changes and all of the opposite or opposing forces in nature from the protons and electrons of the atoms to the movements of the galaxies.

An ancient Chinese classic *Lu Chih Ch'un Ch'iu* (The Annals of Spring and Autumn), written by Lii Pu Wei around 200 B.C., says that we are born when the combining of yin and yang produces our personal Ki energy and we die when yin and yang separate, returning that energy to its source. The same book also states that during our lifetime we are constantly receiving the Ki of yin and yang from the sun, the earth, the food we eat, the air we breathe and the water we drink. Abundant health results when our bodies maintain a harmonious balance and a plentiful supply of Ki. Illness results when we lose that harmony and deplete our supply of Ki.

Even today the Japanese word for disease is *byōki*, which means "Ki got sick." Illness in Japanese characters may be literally read as "diseased Ki." If a person is fatigued or listless he is said to have minus Ki. Minus Ki can also make a person feel depressed or moody.

The Ki energy flow was discovered by sages and healers in ancient China who observed that energy moved in a predictable way throughout the human body and that by using sharp objects to impede or enhance energy flow they could promote healing. They documented the traditional acupuncture points which have not varied for centuries (see Chapter 6). It is interesting to note that modern electronic instruments now enable us to locate these points as the ancient Chinese showed them to be.

Ki energy is seen by practitioners of Oriental medicine to flow along pathways called *meridians* that traverse the body in a fixed pattern somewhat like the network of a complex railway system. These meridians were named for the organ or function served by each section of the pathway. This system was first documented 4,000 years ago in what may be the first medical book ever written, the *Huang-di Nei Jing* or *The Yellow Emperor's Classic of Internal Medicine*. This book has been called the Bible of Chinese medicine. It has been modified in later eras and contains a complete description of Ki energy. According to *The Yellow Emperor's Classic of Internal Medicine*, Ki is always in constant motion in the body and has four primary directions: ascending, descending, entering, and leaving. The book further states: "For optimum health Ki must be free to travel in four directions. Without entering and leaving there is no development, without ascending and descending no transformation, absorption or storing."

Although the idea of a life energy force may be unfamiliar to many, it is by no means new in Western culture. The list of scientists and philosophers who have experimented with and written about it is long and illustrious.

In Austria, Mesmer called it "animal magnetism"; in Germany, Baron von Reichenbach called it "odic force." In America, Wilhelm Reich saw it as "orgone energy" and in Russia, Inyushin called it "bioplasm." It is also apparent that the use of acupuncture, biofeedback, and relaxation techniques using visualization, is gradually becoming established within the framework of Western holistic healing arts. All of the above disciplines involve directing and balancing energy flows within the human body.

The main purpose of this book is to provide the reader with an understanding of Ki energy and to present all of the many ways one can use this knowledge to attain and maintain abundant health and energy for a lifetime. We have therefore included a comprehensive variety of Eastern and Western concepts because, in our opinion, looking at one point of view only can be somewhat limiting. It is of value to compare both Eastern and Western concepts to discover their uniformities and differences. In the comparison we have found that most modern Japanese would claim that the Western concept simply reflects the scientific point of view. Conversely, the Eastern concepts do not always agree with each other, however, they do have one thing in common—in the East, man is seen to be an integral part of the universe and as such, man is viewed as a total entity consisting of mind, body, and spirit. From the Western point of view this may not be applicable to an "energy raising" process. In order to determine whether or not a program or a system is valid it is important to experience it first hand.

We have, therefore, included a wealth of information from both the Eastern and Western points of view which will enable you to choose from a variety of modalities from both cultures that are well known and widely used. We are certain that your experience in working with *Ki: Energy for Everybody* will be a positive one. As you begin to discover who YOU are in relation to the Ki energy of the universe with your body, you will begin to recognize for yourself the wisdom of the ancient concept, "This is Me."

The Western Concept

If you were to look up the definition of energy in a dictionary or an encyclopedia you would find the following description:

> Energy is the capacity of matter to perform work as the result of its motion or position." Energy associated with motion is known as *kinetic* energy while stored energy is called *potential* energy. For example, your muscles utilize kinetic energy when you are physically active. When in a resting state your body is like a battery which stores potential energy, holding it in readiness for use when needed.

There is also a parallel definition which involves the many different kinds of energy. It is the principle of conversion of energy which tells us that energy can neither be created nor destroyed. It is interchangeable according to various laws. For example, when wood is burned, chemical energy is changed into the energy of heat and light.

We are all familiar with the variety of forms of energy that exist in nature such as the light energy of the sun, nuclear energy in uranium, electrical energy in lightning storms, heat energy in fires, and chemical energy in oil. Of all the different kinds of energy, chemical, electrical, and molecular energy are constantly required to maintain your body's basic needs.

The following will give you an overview of the complexity of your energy requirements and an understanding of how the fluctuations of energy within your body can and do determine your changing states of being.

Your body appears solid and opaque, but if it were possible to magnify the cells, molecules, and atoms of which you are composed, it would become apparent that at the most fundamental level you are made up of energy. Your entire being is constantly commingling with gravity, temperature, the general environment, and climate. These factors, along with the nutrients available to you, sunlight or the lack of it, the amount and quality of the air you breathe, your body's flexibility and strength, your body weight, muscle tension, general state of health, and the functioning of your organs, all have a direct bearing upon your energy quotient.

You use part of the energy you take in to maintain and repair your body. Without a conscious effort you are constantly using energy to maintain a narrow internal temperature range (around 98.6°F / 37°C), as circulating blood brings heat to cold areas; secreting digestive juices for the breakdown and absorption of food; synthesizing chemicals which are sent to your internal organs; producing electrochemical impulses which travel throughout your nervous system; replacing worn tissue and blood cells; repairing wounds and mending bones; moving muscles which control digestion, respiration, elimination, and reproduction; radiating heat and eliminating waste products.

On both the conscious and subconscious levels you are also collecting countless bits of information about your environment. The information is gathered by your five major senses which are: touch, taste, smell, sight, and hearing. In addition, there are the less tangible inputs: emotional/spiritual information such as love, attention, caring, enthusiasm, and extra-sensory data. You are the channel or the transformer of these energy sources. As all of this information is processed, the brain determines how much energy is required each and every moment.

You use nerves from the eye to the brain to perceive the form and movement of objects. Passing through this same pathway of eye to brain is the energy of full spectrum light which contains all colors. This energy is processed through the epithelial cells of the eye to photoelectric cells in the brain and relayed to the pituitary gland. This gland is known as the "master gland" because of its role in regulating the functions of the body through its hormonal secretions. Located in the center of your forehead, it plays a crucial role in regulating and distributing energy.

To hear the sounds around you, your inner ears contain bony structures and channels that send vibrations both to and from the brain. For smell and taste, the nose and tongue cooperate to aid the brain in interpreting the energies relayed through these senses. Your sense of touch employs a combination of sensitive areas called upon to decode all tactile data. Through the sense of touch you can distinguish danger from safety and separate pain from pleasure. Your mind and body are also affected by the generation of emotions and by your thoughts.

To keep all of these processes functioning smoothly you need to frequently replenish your supply of energy. The Western concept of how one may do this is the subject of many books and much current research. In essence, these sources tell you that you should:

- Eat three balanced meals a day.
- Take regular exercise at least three times a week and engage in some form of recreational activity as often as your schedule permits.
- Have periodic physical checkups and take medications that balance your body's chemistry when necessary.
- Understand and practice weight control.
- Keep your blood pressure and cholesterol levels down and learn stress management techniques that will help you to cope with the tensions and aggravations in your life.

There is great value to be derived from following this advice; not only in the context of living each day to the fullest but to live it in a healthy and well-functioning body.

The Eastern Concept

In the Eastern traditions energy is seen as Ki, a vital life-force that flows throughout your body. This energy can become abundantly available to you in two ways: The first is to develop an understanding of this energy and an awareness of its existence, the second is to experience it for yourself through many of the "Ki raising" techniques that are in daily use in each of the Oriental societies. Coupled with the above recommendations from the Western traditions, these techniques can become an additional source of energy and well-being.

As we have noted in the section, "Understanding Ki," in Oriental art, medicine and philosophy, everything is classified under the two systems of yin and yang. To maintain harmony and order, it is necessary to keep yin and yang in delicate balance. As Ki is replenished it moves in a predictable way throughout the human body linking the various tissues, organs, and brain functions into a unified whole. It also links a person to his or her environment.

Ki was discovered by sages and healers in ancient times who meditated upon the human fetus inside the womb. They observed that the fetus literally "breathes" through the umbilical cord from the mother into its own navel. This point, or a point slightly below the navel, is thus said to be the starting point for the flow of Ki and remains the point of strongest energy storage and circulation in the adult.

After birth the energy settles into areas of the body which are predominately hot (yang) and cold (yin). In the womb the yin and yang energy is in perfect balance and harmony. However, during the growth process the hot yang energy gradually rises to the upper part of the body which contains the vital organs such as the heart, liver, lungs, and brain while the cold or yin energy settles in the legs,

Fig. 2

Yin
negative
passive
female
receptive
dark
night
cold
soft
wet
winter
shadow

Yin and Yang

Yang
positive
active
male
creative
light
day
heat
hard
dry
summer
sun

genitals, kidneys, and lower abdomen. As one ages, the energy routes become progressively blocked resulting in general fatigue, weakness, and poor health. By reopening the energy routes, it is possible to nourish all parts of the body thereby restoring health and vitality and a sense of rejuvenation.

Many techniques for balancing yin and yang and circulating Ki are given throughout each of the following chapters. The remainder of this chapter looks at the way the Eastern systems perceive energy as it circulates throughout the body.

The Organ Meridians

Just as blood flows throughout your body through a system of blood vessels, arteries, capillaries, and veins, vital energy is seen by practitioners of Oriental medicine to have a definite predictable route throughout the body. It flows along pathways that traverse the body in a fixed pattern somewhat like the network of a complex railway system. The energy travels along this network in pathways divided into major routes called meridians. These meridians were named for the organ or function served by each section of the pathway.

The Ki energy of the body flows both externally, just below the surface of the skin, and internally, within the deeper tissues and organs. The Oriental healing classics tell us that when the Ki flows freely through these pathways in a steady and harmonious way, being neither too active (yang) nor too passive (yin), a state of balance and vibrant health spontaneously occurs.

In Chapter 6 you will find a more detailed description of the acupuncture/acupressure points that are located along each of the meridians. These points are essentially points of high electrical conductivity or, conversely, low electrical resistance. They act somewhat like amplifiers, passing the Ki along from one point to another.

Chinese acupuncture books describe over a thousand of these points. To make it possible to clarify the function and specific properties of each point, the Chinese classified them into twelve main groups. All the acupuncture points belonging to any one of these groups are joined by a line, or *Jing*, in Chinese word which means a "passage" or "meridian."

The number of acupuncture points along each of the meridians varies. For example, the heart meridian has nine points on each side and the bladder meridian has sixty-seven.

The meridians on one side of the body are duplicated by those on the other, just as we have a left as well as a right arm or leg. The twelve main meridians are those of the:

Lung	Bladder
Large intestine	Kidney
Stomach	Pericardium or heart constrictor
Spleen	Triple warmer
Heart	Gallbladder
Liver	Small intestine

There are also two additional unpaired meridians; the conception vessel which runs up the midline of the body in front, and the governing vessel which runs up the midline of the body in the back.

Each meridian receives its Ki energy from another meridian and passes it on to a third, so that the Ki circulates through the meridians in the same way that blood circulates through the blood vessels. The circulation of blood varies more radically, however. For example, after a meal, there will be an increased amount of blood in the vessels supplying the stomach and intestines. Or, when the weather is hot, there will be an increased supply to the skin so that heat can be lost from the body. The flow of Ki through the meridians, conversely, appears to be controlled by a strict "biological clock."

The Ki energy cycle for all twelve meridians is twenty-four hours and a crest of energy flows through each of the meridians at set and measurable times. This creates a daily rhythm which is in harmony with the position of the sun.

Fig. 3   The Body Clock

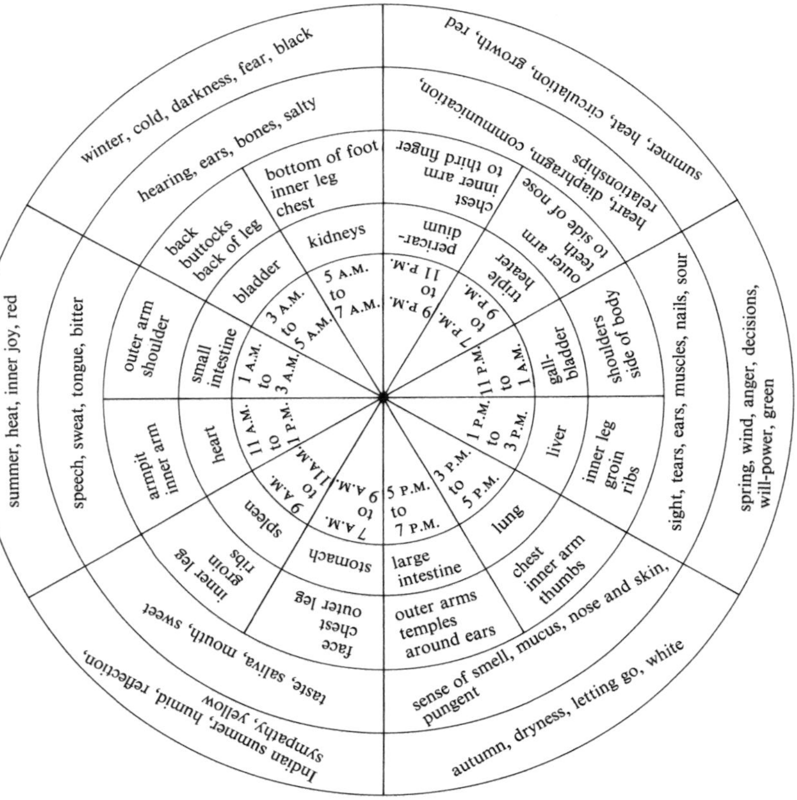

Legend (from the inside to the outside)
1. Time of day
2. Name of the meridian
3. Brief route description
4. Association: sense, fluid, part of the body, taste
5. Season, climate, emotion, color

Although everyone's daily pattern varies slightly, some similarities can be noted. For example, many people feel that the late afternoon is a low energy time of day. In the Western tradition the explanation most often given for this condition is that between lunch and dinnertime one's blood sugar drops causing noticeable fatigue. The Eastern explanation is based on the body clock.

Looking at the body clock you can see that the bladder meridian is most active between three and five in the late afternoon. This meridian accumulates a great deal of our physical and emotional tensions. These become more intense as the crest of energy flows through the meridian.

The body clock illustrates a relationship between the meridians, the parts of the body where these meridians flow, and the times when this meridian is most active.

The Dantian

In the East, from ancient times, it has been thought that the mind and body are both born of the Ki of the universe. The mind is seen as unrefined body, and the body as unrefined mind. The mind is formless, colorless, odorless, and flies from place to place at will. The body has shape, color, odor and its movements are restricted. To keep mind and body unified it is felt to be necessary to first focus the mind. In these cultures, the center of the universe is said to reside in the abdomen and therefore, by concentrating on this point, mind and body come together in a strong and powerful way.

It is a well-known fact that if an object's balancing point is close to the ground, it becomes stable and centered. Conversely, an unbalanced foundation will not stand long and the simplest stress can bring it crashing down. In the Oriental way of thinking, a lack of balance and serenity can occur when your energy is concentrated in the upper body, especially in a racing mind. However, when your consciousness is centered in the *Dantian*, which is located approximately three inches below your navel, you feel very stable and secure. At the same time, you also experience a high level of vitality and abundant energy. It is further thought that all actions that call for strength and stability should naturally be performed from the Dantian. In Japan, for example, *shiatsu*, Noh drama, calligraphy, *sumi-e* brush painting, flower arranging, the tea ceremony, and all of the martial arts are practiced with the attention focused there.

In the Eastern traditions, the Dantian is considered the earth or root of the body. It is seen as the origin of vital energy because it is here that digestion occurs and food is broken down to be converted into energy.

It is also in this region that the developing embryo grows and receives the energizing charge vital to its growth and development.

The Dantian takes its name from the pattern made as several meridians cross at the abdomen, making lines resembling the Chinese character 田 (*den*). One of the reasons that the Dantian is used as a center of focus is because it is here that many autonomic nerves are gathered. By centering attention at this point, the nerves and accompanying blood vessels become regulated which, in turn, helps to regulate the body's basal metabolism.

The Oriental traditions share the belief that a mind without a strong center of focus is easily moved in every direction. Because the body is thought to follow the mind, strength and vitality can suffer if the mind is not brought under control. They further believe that by placing attention on the "one point," the mind automatically concentrates on the sixth *chakra* or "third-eye" (called *Tentei*, in Japanese). Many of the breathing techniques given in Chapter 3, the exercises in Chapter 4 and the relaxation exercises in Chapter 5 include the concept of focusing on the "one point."

The Five Elements or Wu-Hsing

Over two thousand years ago, the Chinese Naturalist School (Yin-Yang Chia), developed the theory of *Wu-Hsing*, or theory of the Five Elements. The five elements (water, fire, wood, metal, and earth) were not considered types of inactive matter, but dynamic processes which were basic to an understanding of the natural world. This theory reflects the rhythms of nature and the varying energies of all the elements. As explained in *The Yellow Emperor's Classic of Internal Medicine*, the five elements represent the five universal forces and the characteristic quality of each element was derived from the careful observation of natural events. Thus, water has the properties of soaking and descending (since water flows downward). Fire both heats and moves upward (since flames rise into the air). Wood allows its form to be shaped into straight or curved pieces. Metal can be melted, molded, and then hardened. Earth's properties include the provision of nourishment through sowing and reaping.

For centuries the five elements have been used in many of the Oriental healing systems. Over time, four major principles describing the changes and interrelationships among the elements were developed: mutual creation, mutual closeness, mutual destruction, and mutual fear.

According the principle of mutual creation, the five elements produce each other: "Wood creates fire, fire creates earth, earth creates metal, metal creates water, and water creates wood." Wood creates fire since fire results from rubbing two pieces of wood together, and wood burns easily. In leaving ashes which become part of the soil, fire creates earth. Observations that metallic ores are found in the earth led to the conclusion that earth creates metal. Metal creates water because metal mirrors exposed at night (a ritual Chinese practice) collect dew, or because metal when heated becomes liquid. Finally, water creates wood by nourishing the growth of plants.

The same pairs of elements are related to each other by the principle of mutual closeness. Each element is considered to be attracted to its source: wood is close to water, water to metal, metal to earth, earth to fire, and fire to wood. Thus the interaction and relationship between these pairs of elements is also closely related to the balance and harmony of nature.

The principle of mutual destruction describes the series of conflicts between pairs of elements. Wood weakens earth by removing nutrients from the soil. Earth limits water by causing natural boundaries near water such as the shores of lakes, rivers or oceans. Water extinguishes fire. Fire conquers metal by melting it. Metal, in the form of axes and knives, can cut down trees and carve wood. Therefore, by the principle of mutual fear, an element respects or fears the element that could destroy it. Wood fears metal, metal fire, fire water, water earth, and earth fears wood.

The similarities and differences among these principles can best be understood in terms of yin and yang. Creation and closeness, both constructive principles, are considered yang; whereas, destruction and fearfulness, their opposites, are viewed as yin.

In addition to representing forces in the natural world, the five elements provide guiding principles for diagnosis and therapy in traditional Oriental medicine. In the human body the internal organs are divided into two groups: The six yin or solid organs and the six yang or hollow organs. Each of the yin and yang organs are identified with one of the elements. The heart (yin) and small intestine (yang) are associated with fire, the spleen (yin) and stomach (yang) with earth, the lungs (yin) and large intestine (yang) with metal, the kidney (yin) and bladder (yang) with water, and the liver (yin) and gallbladder (yang) with wood.

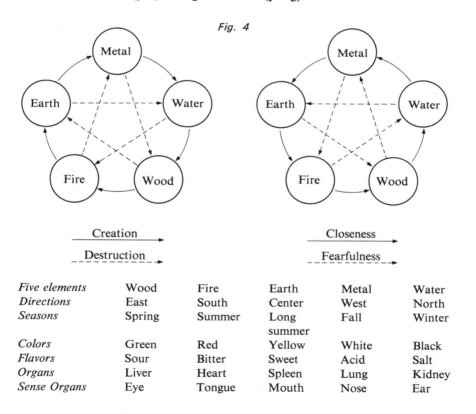

Fig. 4

Five elements	Wood	Fire	Earth	Metal	Water
Directions	East	South	Center	West	North
Seasons	Spring	Summer	Long summer	Fall	Winter
Colors	Green	Red	Yellow	White	Black
Flavors	Sour	Bitter	Sweet	Acid	Salt
Organs	Liver	Heart	Spleen	Lung	Kidney
Sense Organs	Eye	Tongue	Mouth	Nose	Ear

Chinese physicians began applying the theory of the five elements to the maintenance of health and the cure of illness thousands of years ago. In time, clinical experience led to the development of sophisticated theories based on the five elements. For example, the five element medical model stresses interrelationships among the internal organs rather than their individual functioning. Using the principles of mutual creation and mutual destruction, Chinese medicine explains that both an excess as well as a deficiency in a specific organ may have a broader effect upon other organ functions as well. Western medicine often seeks to cure symptoms by treating only the diseased organ rather than considering the interrelationships between all of the organs. In contrast, Oriental medicine focuses on the ability of the body to balance and heal itself by harmonizing the energies of the interrelating organ functions. This is also true in the use of the five element theory which is widely in use in China today for classifying and distributing herbal medicines. By sensitively evaluating both the effects of the medicines and the needs of the patient, a Chinese physician attempts to establish a wholeness and balance that assists the body to regain a high degree of homeostasis.

The Chakras

According to the ancient Indian sages, the human body has thirteen subtle energy centers called *chakras*. Chakra is the Sanskrit word for "wheel"; the word was chosen because the sages described them as fast moving vortices of energy. Six of the chakras are minor in their activities, and seven are major. For our purposes we will concentrate on the major chakras.

In the Eastern traditions the human spine is regarded as the mystical link between God and man. The chakras are seen as storage centers for *prana* or Ki. The first chakra is located at the base of the spine and represents man's lowest nature; the uppermost chakra is located at the top of the skull and symbolizes the highest spirituality.

Fig. 5

Each chakra relates to the endocrine system and to a specific organ which is influenced by that chakra's energy field. Chakras can be thought of as dynamos through which energy is received and transmitted. Each of the chakras vibrates at a characteristic frequency and has been described to be predominately of a certain color which corresponds to the frequency of the vibration. In the following illustration you will be able to see the location of each of the major chakras and to note its function and characteristics.

The location and function of each of the chakras, as well as a description of its characteristics, is given below.

Muladhara Chakra

Name:	First Chakra
	Muladhara (*mul*—root, *adhara*—place)
Location:	Base of the spine
Color:	Red

The *muladhara* chakra is connected to the sacral plexus, the rectum, the prostate gland, and the male reproductive organs. It is also called the *Kundalini* or physical chakra, because its energy vitalizes the entire body. It is considered to be the origin of all sexual energy.

Once awakened, the *Kundalini* energy ascends the spinal column, called the *sushumna nadi*, and activates the remaining chakras.

Swadhisthana Chakra

Name:	Second Chakra
	Swadhisthana (*swa*—self, *sthan*—dwelling place)
Location:	Three finger's width below the navel
Color:	Orange

The second chakra is related to the prostatic plexus, the adrenal glands, the female reproductive organs, and the kidneys. In Japan this center is called the Dantian and in China it is known as the *tang tien*. It is thought to govern the impulses of creativity and sexuality. It is also the generating center of physical energy.

Manipura Chakra

Name:	Third Chakra
	Manipura (*mani*—jewel, *pura*—city)
Location:	Slightly above the navel
Color:	Yellow

The third chakra is associated with the solar plexus, the spleen, the pancreas, the liver, and the gallbladder. It is also called the "abdominal brain" because it is the place where we carry our emotions and make decisions. It is from this chakra that we express thoughts such as "a gut level feeling."

Anahata Chakra

Name:	Fourth Chakra
	Anahata Chakra (*an*—not, *ahat*—struck)
Location:	Center of the chest
Color:	Green

The fourth chakra is called the heart chakra. It is connected to the cardiac plexus, the thymus gland, and the pericardium. It controls respiration and also relates to joyfulness and love. It is the place where the energies of mind, body, and spirit come together. There are three chakras below it and three above it making it the place of perfect union.

Vishudhi Chakra

Name:	Fifth Chakra
	Vishudhi (*vishudhi*—to purify)
Location:	Center of the throat
Color:	Blue

The fifth chakra relates to the thyroid gland, at the level of the throat, which regulates the basal metabolism (the amount of energy used by the body at rest). It controls speech and sound and therefore is the center of communication and self-expression.

Ajna Chakra

Name:	Sixth Chakra
	Ajna (*ajna*—to command)
Location:	Center of the forehead
Color:	Indigo

This chakra controls the autonomic nervous system and is associated with the pineal gland which is located between the eyebrows. It is the seat of the mystical "third eye."

Sahasrara Chakra

Name:	Seventh Chakra
	Sahasrara (*sahasrara*—beyond all elements)
Location:	Top of the head
Color:	Violet

The seventh chakra corresponds with the pituitary gland and the cortical layer of the brain. It is thought to govern spiritual consciousness because it is the goal of the *Kundalini* energy to unite with the energy of the *Sahasrara*. When this center is opened, supreme bliss and universal energy combine in "the thousand petalled lotus." In China it is also referred to as "the hundred meeting place" because there are said to be one hundred energies that flow upward to meet at the top of the skull.

Eating

The Western Concept

Currently many dietary changes are being advocated in the United States. For example, in 1977 the U.S. Senate Select Committee on Nutrition and Human Needs released a report called *Dietary Goals for Americans* that advocated a change in our eating habits.

A preface to the Dietary Goals includes the following:

> The diet of the American people has become increasingly rich in meat, other sources of saturated fat and cholesterol, and in sugar. The diet we eat today was not planned or developed for any particular purpose. It is a happenstance related to our farmers and the activities of our food industry. The risks associated with eating this diet are demonstrably large. The question to be asked, therefore, is not why would we change our diet but why not? Heart disease, cancer, diabetes and hypertension are the diseases that kill us. They are epidemic in our population. We cannot afford to temporize.

Other nations that share our dietary habits such as the industrialized countries of Europe, Canada, and Scandinavia experience the same illnesses in about the same proportion as their populations. In contrast, there are many countries that do not share our eating habits or our illnesses. It is a well-known fact that diets rich in starches and vegetable sources of protein, and lower in meats, fats, and sugars are more conducive to good health.

After making an extensive search through many of the current diet and nutrition books and magazines and after contacting several well-known nutritionists to discover their views on this important subject, we have found that most people who are looking for diet information have three goals in common: The first is to be healthy and to fight diseases such as heart disease and cancer. The second is to eliminate extra pounds and the third is to increase one's chances for a longer and more productive life. Few of these sources include an in-depth evaluation of the amount of energy that is to be gained from making careful nutritional choices. Therefore, our approach is somewhat different. We do not advocate that you "go on a diet" for any reason. Our only goal is to start you on

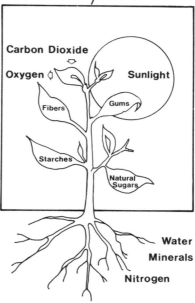

Fig. 6

PHOTOSYNTHESIS

Carbon Dioxide

Oxygen

Sunlight

Fibers

Gums

Starches

Natural Sugars

Water

Minerals

Nitrogen

the path of *eating for energy* because we feel that all of the other desired results will be brought about naturally when you understand how your food choices can directly influence your stamina and vitality.

Before we examine these choices in detail, let us first explore the way the food you eat provides energy for your body. There are many complex reactions that must occur in this process, however we would like to begin this section with an overview which will enhance your ability to make fuller use of the material in this and other sections.

How You Change Food into Energy

The sun is the ultimate source of all energy on earth. Plants use this energy to take in carbon, hydrogen, oxygen, and nitrogen from their environment and, through a process called *photosynthesis*, manufacture either carbohydrate, fat, or protein. The foods then become stored energy and when consumed are broken down by the digestive process into simple compounds which can be absorbed into your body and transported to various cells. The cells, in turn, transform the chemical energy of these simple compounds into more complex ones that may be stored for future use in the forms of glycogen or fat, or used immediately if needed.

We have all experienced sparkling weather, beautiful scenery or pleasant company. All of these bring about a state of well-being. Even among the best of these pleasures however, some limits are set by your nutritional state. You can feel good only when your blood sugar (glucose) level is right. If that condition is not met, neither the most beautiful place nor the most stimulating companion can compensate.

To function properly your nerves, brain, and every cell in your body must have a constant supply of energy which is supplied in the form of glucose. Glucose, from the Greek *glyks*, meaning "sweet," is a sugar that occurs widely in nature and is the usual form in which carbohydrate is assimilated by man and animals.

When the blood's supply of sugar is low, there are two ways it can be raised. Your body can convert newly digested food into blood sugar or it can draw upon its supply of stored energy.

When you wake up in the moring your blood glucose level is low because your cells must draw upon the remaining supply to do their work. When you eat, your blood sugar level rises again. If you choose to eat a meal that is high in refined (simple) carbohydrate such as syrup or granulated sugar, your level may rise too high and then drop sharply because refined carbohydrates are rapidly digested. Whenever you have an oversupply of sugar in your blood, your pancreas and liver begin to withdraw the excess in order to keep your blood sugar at a desirable level. The excess energy is then converted into glycogen and stored in the liver or in muscle tissue. It can also be stored as fat in adipose tissue when your caloric intake exceeds your energy demands. During the hours that follow, before you eat again, the stored glycogen (but not fat) is used to replenish your glucose supply as the brain and other body cells use it to meet their energy needs.

In order to better understand this fascinating process, let us start at the beginning, at the cellular level, to see how your energy is produced.

The basic ingredients you need to produce energy are oxygen and glucose. All of the chemical processes which occur within your body are either aerobic (occurring in the presence of oxygen) or anaerobic (without oxygen). When oxygen and glucose come together in your cells, they ignite in a chemical reaction that releases energy. About 55 percent of the energy becomes ATP (adenosine triphosphate), a chemical energy, which is available to be converted into whatever energy form the cell requires to do its work. The remaining 45 percent is released as heat energy to provide your minimal body temperature. Waste products, carbon dioxide, and water are also formed.

ATP-like compounds are necessary to power the two classes of activity which consume energy each day. The first are vital processes which go on all the time, even during sleep; the maintenance of your heartbeat, respiration, nerve function, glandular activity, generation of heat, and all other involuntary processes. (This is called your basal metabolism.) The second are the voluntary activities over which you have conscious control; sitting, standing, running, eating, and so on. We will refer often to the roles of ATP in the exercise section of this book.

The constant action of all physical and chemical changes that take place within your body is called *metabolism*. The primary purpose of metabolism is to provide energy for your body's cells. The energy in food is found in the bonds that hold the atoms of nutrients together. In some ways, the metabolism of the nutrients is like the various transformations that can be performed with Tinkertoys. Imagine that the wheels are atoms and the sticks are electrons. During metabolism your body goes to work with an "electron saw" and breaks these bonds, actually separating the atoms from one another. When the atoms are separated two things can happen. Simple compounds can be put together to form larger, more complex structures. (This building-up process is called *anabolism*.) Or larger units may be broken apart and reduced to simple materials. (This is called *catabolism*.) Anabolism refers to the synthesis of cellular materials for growth, maintenance, and repair of body tissues. Catabolism is the process of breaking down cellular material into smaller units either for energy production or excretion. Both processes occur simultaneously throughout life.

Life and Energy

All living things constantly need to replenish their supply of energy. For example, plants survive on inorganic (non-living) material. They use chemicals drawn from the soil and the air and then process them in the presence of sunlight. They can build up complex substances out of simple ones. Man and animals, however, use fewer natural inorganic substances within their bodies. For them, a balanced supply of carbohydrates, fats, proteins, vitamins, minerals, and water is necessary to maintain health and vitality. Of these, carbohydrates, fats, and proteins are necessary for energy. Proteins, minerals, and water are used for growth and repair while the body processes require proteins, minerals, vitamins, and water.

The constituents of food that help growth and repair cannot all be measured on one scale because different constituents do different jobs, which are not interchangeable. The same applies to the constituents that control body processes. However,

Fig. 7

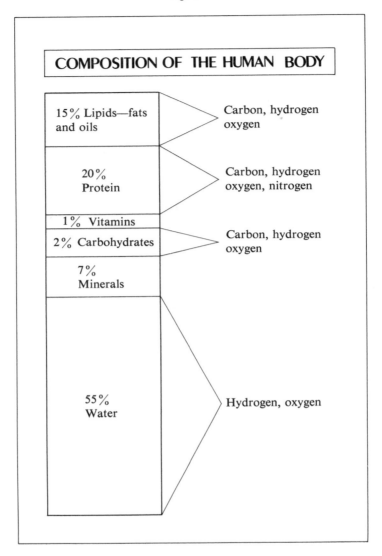

the constituents that provide energy can be measured on a single scale and added together. All of them can be measured in terms of the amount of heat they produce in the body.

Fig. 8

HUMAN NUTRIENT REQUIREMENTS

MAiN NUTRiENTS · individual COMPONENTS of MAiN NUTRiENTS

MAiN NUTRiENTS	%	individual COMPONENTS of MAiN NUTRiENTS
CARBOHYDRATES SUGARS & STARCH	60%	MONO-SACCHARIDES: GLUCOSE FRUCTOSE GALACTOSE DI-SACCHARIDES: SUCROSE MALTOSE LACTOSE POLY-SACCHARIDES: GLYCOGEN CELLULOSE STARCH PECTIN
PROTEINS ESSENTIAL AMINO ACIDS OTHER AMINO ACIDS	20%	ARGININE HISTIDINE ISOLEUCINE LEUCINE LYSINE METHIONINE PHENYLALANINE THREONINE TRYPTOPHAN VALINE CYSTINE GLUTAMIC ACID GLYCINE SERINE IODOGORGOIC ACID PROLINE HYDROXYPROLINE TYROSINE ALANINE ASPARTIC ACID
LIPIDS FATS & OILS	15%	MONO-UNSATURATED: OLEIC ACID POLY-UNSATURATED: LINOLEIC ACID LINOLENIC ACID ARACHIODONIC ACID SATURATED: STEARIC ACID
MAJOR MINERALS **TRACE MINERALS**	4%	CALCIUM PHOSPHORUS POTASSIUM SULPHUR CHLORINE SODIUM FLUORINE MAGNESIUM IRON MANGANESE SILICON COPPER IODINE ZINC COBALT MOLYBDENUM SELENIUM VANADIUM
VITAMINS	1%	VITAMIN A VITAMIN B1,B2,B3,B5,B6,B12,B15, VITAMIN C VITAMIN D VITAMIN E VITAMIN K BIOTIN CHOLINE FOLIC ACID INOSITOL

Calories

The basic unit for measuring any energy (including heat output) is the calorie. This is defined as the amount of energy needed to raise the temperature of 1 cc of water by 1 degree centigrade. The measure used in talking about food and human energy need is a thousand times larger than this. It is the kilocalorie, or calorie. By refer- ' ring to the chart you can see how many calories you use up in a day. Remember that charts are based on averages and do not provide specific information, however, it is interesting to determine, within an average range, where you fit in. The number of calories also represents the amount of energy your food must supply.

Age	Men	Women
19–22	2,900 (2,500–3,300)	2,100 (1,700–2,500)
23–50	2,700 (2,300–3,100)	2,000 (1,600–2,400)
51–75	2,400 (2,000–2,800)	1,800 (1,400–2,200)
76+	2,050 (1,650–2,450)	1,600 (1,200–2,000)

Fig. 9

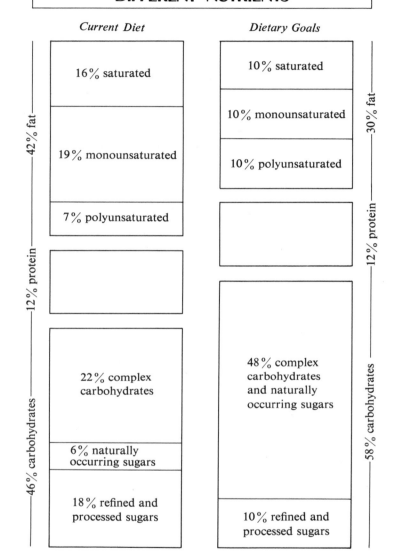

PERCENT OF CALORIES FROM DIFFERENT NUTRIENTS

Current Diet   *Dietary Goals*

Current Diet:
- 42% fat — 16% saturated, 19% monounsaturated, 7% polyunsaturated
- 12% protein
- 46% carbohydrates — 22% complex carbohydrates, 6% naturally occurring sugars, 18% refined and processed sugars

Dietary Goals:
- 30% fat — 10% saturated, 10% monounsaturated, 10% polyunsaturated
- 12% protein
- 58% carbohydrates — 48% complex carbohydrates and naturally occurring sugars, 10% refined and processed sugars

How Much Should You Weigh?

Many people try to determine how much they should weigh by reading height-weight tables, but since these tables often indicate average weights, rather than optimum weights, the figures tend to be too high. There is, however, a formula for estimating your healthiest weight.

Adult women of average build can compute their ideal weight by multiplying their height in inches by 3.5 and then subtracting 110 pounds ($60 \times 3.5 - 110 = 100$). For men of average build the formula is height in inches by 4, minus 130. A six-foot man should weight about 158.

It is important to make allowances for bone structure and muscularity. Two people of the same height may have totally different bone structures and therefore should not weigh the same amount. But be careful that in making these allowances, you do not mistake fat for muscle. And remember that if you are 30 pounds over-weight, it is unlikely that the difference is all in your bones.

The amount of food you need to maintain your ideal weight depends upon how active you are. Begin by rating yourself on the scale below:

> 13—very inactive
> 14—slightly inactive
> 15—moderately active
> 16—relatively active
> 17—frequently, strenuously active

If you are a sedentary office worker or a housewife you should probably rate yourself a 13. If your physical exercise consists of occasional games of golf or an afternoon walk, you are a 14. A score of 15 means that you frequently engage in moderate exercise—jogging, calisthenics, tennis. A 16 requires that you are almost always on the go, seldom sitting down or standing still for long. Do not give yourself a 17 unless you are a construction worker or engage in other strenuous activity frequently. Most adult Americans should rate themselves 13 or 14.

To calculate the number of calories you need to maintain your ideal weight, multiply your activity rate by your ideal weight. A 200 pound office worker, for example, needs 2,600 calories a day; a 200 pound athlete needs 3,400 calories.

To estimate how many calories you are getting now, multiply your current weight times your activity level. If your weight is constant at 140 pounds and you are inactive, you are consuming about 1,820 calories a day (13×140). Subtract the number of calories you need for your ideal weight from the number of calories you are consuming, and you will know the size of your energy imbalance.

To reach your ideal weight, you should correct your imbalance slowly. It is a good idea to lose no more than 1 percent of your current weight per week. Regardless of your weight, you should not consume less than 1,200 calories a day. Reducing by much more than 1 percent of your body weight a week could mean destruction of muscles and organs as well as fat.

The Essential Nutrients

Sources of Energy (Calories)

Carbohydrates and fats are the primary sources of energy while protein is a significant secondary source. These foods supply the necessary fuel for body heat and work. They are composed of large molecular complexes of various combinations of carbon, hydrogen, oxygen, and, in the case of protein, nitrogen.

Carbohydrates

Carbohydrates derive their name from the fact that they are made up of carbon, hydrogen, and oxygen with the proportion of hydrogen to oxygen being the same as the proportion found in water, that is, two parts hydrogen to one part oxygen. In essence, carbohydrates are hydrated (water-filled) carbons.

Carbohydrates are our greatest source of energy. They are used for all body functions and muscular exertion and are necessary for the digestion and assimilation of other foods. They provide us with immediate energy by producing heat in the body through the interaction of carbon and oxygen in the bloodstream. Carbohydrates also help regulate protein and fat metabolism; fats require carbohydrates for their breakdown within the liver.

The principal carbohydrates present in foods are sugars, starches, and cellulose. Simple sugars, such as those in honey and fruits, are very easily digested. Other sugars, such as table sugar, require more digestive action, but they are not nearly as complex as starches, including those found in whole grain. Whole grains require prolonged enzymatic action in order to be broken down and assimilated or absorbed by the body. Cellulose, found in the skins of fruits and vegetables, as well as the outer layers of grains, is largely unabsorbable by humans. However, it provides the bulk necessary for intestinal action and also aids elimination.

All sugars and starches are eventually converted by the body into a simple form called "glucose." Some of the glucose (or blood sugar) is used as fuel by tissues of the brain, nervous system, and muscles. A small portion of it is converted to glycogen and stored by the liver and muscles; the excess is converted to fat and stored throughout the body as a reserve source of energy.

Fig. 10

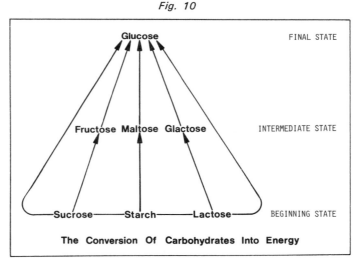

The Conversion Of Carbohydrates Into Energy

You especially need carbohydrates as an essential source of energy for the central nervous system, including the brain. Approximately one-fifth of the energy requirement of your basal metabolic rate is for brain function, and glucose only, not fat, is required for this.

Carbohydrates have a "protein sparing" effect. This means that when carbohydrates are plentiful in your diet you will use them as a source of energy instead of using your precious protein, thereby making the protein available for building and repairing body tissue. It is also much more energy efficient to use carbohydrates in the production of energy than to use protein.

Sources of Carbohydrates

Sugars: Sucrose is found principally in sugar cane, sugar beets, and maple syrup; lactose is found in milk; fructose in fruits.

Starch: Starch is found in seeds such as wheat, rice, oats, corn, peas, and beans; in tubers (underground stems) such as potatoes, and in roots such as yams, sweet potatoes, and cassava. Foods in the bread and cereal group are the major source of starch in our diets.

Fats

Fats, or lipids provide the greatest concentration of energy in your diet. When used by the body, fats provide nine calories per gram compared to the four calories per gram furnished by carbohydrates or proteins.

Fats perform many functions for the body in addition to providing energy. They act as carriers for the fat soluble vitamins, A, D, E, and K. They help make calcium available to body tissues by aiding in the absorption of vitamin D, particularly to your bones and teeth. Fats help the conversion of carotene to vitamin A. Fat deposits surround, protect, and hold your organs in place. A layer of fat insulates your body from environmental temperature changes and preserves body heat.

Fats also create a longer lasting sensation of fullness after a meal (satiety) by slowing down the digestive process. This happens because they slow the stomach's secretion of hydrochloric acid which is used for the digestion of protein.

There are two types of fatty acids, saturated and unsaturated. Fats from animal sources and coconuts are solid at room temperature and are called *saturated* because all of the carbon atoms in their structure have their bonds attached to a hydrogen atom. In other words, it is "saturated" with hydrogen. *Unsaturated* fatty acids have unfilled bonding areas on the carbon atoms. They are usually liquid at room temperature. These come from vegetable, nut, or seed sources such as corn, safflower, sunflowers, and olives. Vegetable shortenings and margarine have undergone a process called *hydrogenation*. This process takes unsaturated oils and converts them to a more solid form of fat.

Fat helps to prevent skin dryness and scaliness. It is also necessary for the transport and breakdown of cholesterol which is a normal component of most body tissues, especially those of the brain and nervous system, liver, and blood.

Sources of Fats

Some primary sources of fat are butter, lard, margarine, meat fats, bacon, oils, nuts, cheese, and cream, and from the plant products, all the grains, soybeans, peanut oil, and olive oil.

Measure Your Body Fat

It is possible to make a reasonably accurate estimate of your body fat by pinching at the areas illustrated in Fig. 11 between finger and thumb. An excess of fat would be a pinch greater than one inch and is a sign that weight should be lost.

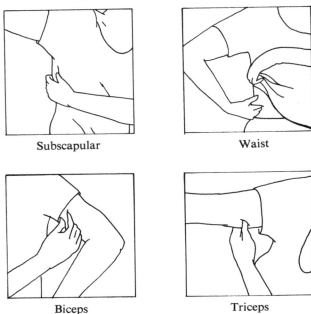

Fig. 11   Measure Your Body Fat

Subscapular   Waist

Biceps   Triceps

Protein

Protein is one of the most important elements in your body. It is of primary importance in the growth and development of all body tissues. It is the major source of the building material needed for muscles, blood, skin, hair, nails, and internal organs, including the heart and the brain.

Protein is necessary for the formation of hormones, which control a variety of body functions such as: growth and rate of metabolism, preventing the blood and tissues from becoming either too acid or too alkaline; and to help regulate the water balance in your body. Enzymes, substances necessary for basic life functions, and antibodies, which help fight foreign substances, are also formed from protein.

As well as being the major source of all building material for your body, protein may be called upon as a source of body heat and to provide energy. If there are sufficient fats and carbohydrates present in your diet, protein is stored instead of being used for energy. In this case, protein that is not used for building tissue is converted by your liver and stored as fat in the body tissues.

During digestion, complex proteins are decomposed into simpler forms called *amino acids*. There are twenty-two varieties of amino acids found in proteins of which eight are called "essential," because they must be supplied by the diet. In order for your body to properly synthesize protein, all the essential amino acids must be present simultaneously and in the proper proportions. If just one essential amino acid is missing, protein synthesis becomes very poor because of the missing link in the chain. When a food contains all the essential amino acids, it is termed a *complete protein*. Most meats and dairy products are complete protein foods, while most vegetables and fruits are incomplete proteins. You must combine foods containing incomplete proteins carefully so that those weak in one essential amino acid will be balanced by foods strong in that same amino acid.

Sources of Protein
Sources of proteins include a variety of meats, fowl, fish, soybeans, milk, eggs, cheese, legumes, bread, cereals, and nuts.

Other Nutrients

Vitamins
At the turn of the century, vitamins were unknown, although people of ancient civilizations recognized the need for certain unknown substances that were necessary in the diet to maintain health. It was not until 1912 that a Polish biochemist named Casimir Funk coined the term *vitamine* to include food substances that were not proteins, carbohydrates, fats, or minerals but were vital to health. In 1920 the word was changed to "vitamin" without the final "e," since these chemicals were not amines, as was first suspected.

We now know of forty vitamins, of which twelve or more are essential in your diet. Because they were not discovered simultaneously, they originally formed a list of letter names to which subscripts were added to identify them. Now their chemical structures have been identified and chemical names are often used for many of them. Identification of their chemical composition has also meant that many of them can now be made artificially.

Like the hormones from the endocrine glands, and the enzymes from the tissues, vitamins regulate life processes. Some vitamins are also part of enzyme chains and act as catalysts. The complex interrelationships between these regulatory substances are just beginning to be understood in-depth.

Because your body is not able to synthesize vitamins, you must rely upon the food you eat to provide a constant supply. Many people are tempted to use vitamin pills as insurance against illness. This should not be necessary if good nutrition guidelines are followed. Vitamin supplements usually contain no more than the recommended daily allowance and their unnecessary use might represent a waste of money. Therapeutic vitamin preparations often contain from three to five times this amount and should be prescribed by a physician since misuse could result in toxicity.

Vitamin potency is indicated in two ways. Vitamin A and D are given as units, most others by weight (either milligrams or micrograms). Every five years the National Research Council's Food and Nutrition Board revises the Recommended Daily Allowances. The RDA provides a safety margin above the minimum daily requirement needed for life and health.

Vitamins are classified by their solubility. Those soluble in fat or oils are called *fat soluble* and include A, D, E, and K. Those that are soluble in water are called *water soluble* and are the B complex group and vitamin C.

General characteristics of fat soluble vitamins include their ability to remain stable at ordinary cooking temperatures although some are altered by light or exposure to air. They are stored in body tissues.

The water soluble vitamins, as the term implies, dissolve in water and are not stored in your body. It is important to include foods that are rich in a wide variety of the water soluble vitamins in your daily diet.

A cluster of vitamins often found together in the same foods and having intricate interrelationships, is called the *vitamin B complex*. There are twelve known members of this group. Because they act as catalysts affecting the speed of body processes, all of the B vitamins are called co-enzymes. Vitamin C is the least stable vitamin. It is altered by cooking temperatures and exposure to air. Interestingly, its value is not lost when food is frozen.

Vitamin Chart

Fat Soluble Vitamins	Function	Food Sources
Vitamin A	Aids eyes and visual processes, promotes growth and vitality, prevents infection, necessary for appetite.	Fruits, deep yellow and dark green vegetables, dairy products, liver, margarine, eggs
Vitamin D	Regulates the use of calcium and phosphorous, essential in avoiding tooth decay, muscular weakness and lack of vigor.	Fat, eggs, milk, seawater fish, cod liver oil, butter. Can also be synthesized with the aid of sunshine.
Vitamin E	Protects some vitamins from being destroyed by oxygen, function not completely known.	Whole grain cereals, all meats, eggs, green leafy vegetables, beans, soybeans, whole wheat, wheat germ oils
Vitamin K	Regulates blood clotting time, necessary for quick healing.	Green leafy vegetables, pork, liver, eggs and milk, some cereal grains. Most important source comes from intestinal bacterial flora.

Water-soluble Vitamins	Function	Food Sources
Vitamin B_1	Aids in digestion, promotes growth, essential for nerves, tissues, the heart muscle. Prevents mental depression, insomnia, irritability, and is essential for carbohydrate metabolism.	Peanuts, whole wheat, oatmeal, pork, milk, and most vegetables
Vitamin B_2 (Riboflavin)	Improves growth and general health, especially healthy eyes, mouth, and skin.	Same as B_1 sources plus cheese

Water-soluble Vitamins	Function	Food Sources
Vitamin B_6 (Pyridoxine)	Necessary in fat and protein metabolism, essential in more than 30 enzyme reactions. Also affects muscular control.	Cantaloupe, cabbage, meat, fish, milk, egg yolk
Vitamin B_{12} (Cobalamin)	Metabolism of folic acid. Formation and regeneration of red blood cells. Necessary to prevent fatigue.	Liver, beef, pork, eggs, cheese, and milk
Niacin (Nicotinic acid) B-complex	Promotes growth and proper function of the nervous system. Necessary for sugar metabolism. Prevents mental depression, insomnia, weakness, and headaches.	Lean meat, whole wheat products, beans, green vegetables
Pantothenic acid B-complex	Synthesis of anti-bodies. Necessary for normal digestive processes.	Wheat, beans, peas, molasses, liver, kidney, yeast
Biotin B-complex	Growth promotion, metabolism of fats, conversion of some amino acids. Helps prevent muscle pain and exhaustion.	Minute amounts found in all foods
Folic acid B-complex	Formation of red blood cells, aids in protein metabolism, contributes to normal growth.	Dark green leafy vegetables, kidney, liver, yeast
Choline B-complex	Regulation of liver function, fat metabolism. Prevents hardening of the arteries.	Egg yolks, liver, wheat germ, brain, heart, beans, green leafy vegetables
Inositol B-complex	Same function as choline.	Fruits, nuts, whole grains, milk, and meat
PABA (Para-amino-benzoic acid)	Promotes growth.	Yeast
Vitamin P	Strengthens walls of the capillaries, prevents destruction of vitamin C by oxidation, builds resistance to infection.	All citrus fruits

Minerals

Minerals are nutrients that exist in your body and in food in organic and inorganic combinations. According to Dr. William A. Fowler, known as the father of astrophysics and winner of the 1983 Nobel Prize in physics, many minerals which are essential for your body's health, have originated in the stars. These elements fall to earth and are processed by plants from the soil in which they grow. He is fond of reminding his audiences that, "apart from hydrogen you are 65 percent oxygen, 18 percent carbon with a smaller percent of nitrogen, sodium, magnesium, phosphorus, sulfur, chlorine, potassium, and traces of still heavier elements, all made

Mineral Chart

Minerals	Function	Food Sources
Calcium	Strengthens structure of bones and teeth; promotes clotting of blood, water balance, muscle contraction, nerve response.	Milk, cheese, leafy green vegetables, clams, oysters, almonds, legumes, water
Chlorine	Provides hydrochloric acid of gastric juice, acid-base balance, activity of muscles and nerves, water balance.	Table salt, water
Chromium	Required for metabolism of blood glucose, fatty acid synthesis, insulin in metabolism.	Corn oil, meat, whole grains
Copper	Required for utilization of iron, enzymes in energy metabolism.	Liver, shellfish, nuts, legumes, water
Fluorine	Provides resistance to development of dental cavities.	Water, naturally occurring or fluoridated
Iodine	Needed for synthesis of thyroxine hormone.	Iodized table salt, water, variable amounts in foods
Iron	Part of hemoglobin, carries oxygen in blood, oxidative enzymes.	Liver, meat, oysters, leafy green vegetables, dried apricots, prunes, peaches, raisins, egg yolks, legumes, nuts, whole grains
Magnesium	Activates enzymes, temperature regulation, nerve and muscle activity, protein synthesis	Whole grains, legumes, nuts, leafy green vegetables
Manganese	Required for enzyme activity, many metabolic functions.	Whole grains, legumes, nuts, leafy green vegetables, meat
Phosphorus	Aids structure of teeth and bones, acid-base balance, energy metabolism.	Liver, meat, eggs, milk, cheese, nuts, legumes, whole grains, refined cereals
Potassium	Promotes water balance, nerve and muscle activity.	Meat, milk, leafy green vegetables, dates, bananas, cantaloupes, apricots, citrus fruits, bamboo shoots, prunes
Sodium	Promotes acid-base balance, water balance, nerve and muscle activity.	Table salt, leavenings, MSG, soy sauce, condiments, milk, cheese, eggs, meat, fish, water
Sulfur	Component of protein, thiamine, and biotin; involved in oxidation reduction reactions.	Meat, eggs, milk, cheese, all foods containing protein
Zinc	Constituent of hormone, insulin; promotes enzyme activity in metabolism.	Oysters, liver, wheat germ, yeast, seafood

Molybdenum, selenium, nickel, tin, vanadium, and silicon have roles in many animal organisms, but man's need for them has not yet been verified.

in stars. Thus it's possible to say that you and your neighbor and I, one of us and all of us, are a little bit of star dust."

Although only 4 or 5 percent of your body weight is mineral matter, minerals are vital to your overall mental and physical well-being. All tissues and internal fluids of living things contain varying quantities of minerals. Minerals are constituents of the bones, teeth, soft tissue, muscle, blood, and nerve cells. They are important factors in maintaining physiological processes, strengthening skeletal structures, and preserving the vigor of your heart and brain, as well as all muscle and nerve systems.

Minerals, like vitamins, act as catalysts for many biological reactions within your body, including muscle response, the transmission of messages through your nervous system, digestion, and metabolism or utilization of nutrients in food. They are also important in the production of hormones.

Minerals coexist with vitamins and their work is interrelated. For example, some B complex vitamins are absorbed only when combined with phosphorus. Vitamin C greatly increases the absorption of iron, and calcium absorption would not occur without vitamin D. Zinc helps vitamin A to be released from the liver. Some minerals are even part of vitamins: vitamin B_1 contains sulfur and B_{12} contains cobalt.

Minerals help to maintain the delicate water balance essential to the proper functioning of mental and physical processes. They keep blood and tissue fluids from becoming either too acid or too alkaline and they assist other nutrients to pass easily into the bloodstream. They also help to draw chemical substances in and out of the cells as well as aid in the creation of antibodies. Calcium, chlorine, phosphorus, potassium, magnesium, sodium, and sulfur are known as the *macrominerals* because they are present in relatively high amounts in your body tissues. They are measured in milligrams. Other minerals, termed *trace minerals*, are present in your body only in the most minute quantities but are essential for your continued good health. These include chromium, copper, fluorine, iodine, iron, manganese, and zinc. Trace minerals are measured in micrograms.

Water

Water is the most important nutrient found in the body because it is responsible for and involved in nearly every body process, including digestion, absorption, circulation, excretion, and maintaining normal body temperature. Every living cell in your body depends on water to carry out its essential functions. Through the blood and lymphatic system, water carries nutrients and oxygen to cells and removes waste products. The body eliminates these metabolic wastes through the water in sweat and urine.

Another important characteristic of water is its incompressibility, that is, its molecules resist being crowded together. Because of this, water acts as a lubricant around joints, it protects sensitive tissue, such as the spinal cord, from shock, it keeps the optimal pressure on the retina and lens of the eye, and lubricates the digestive tract and all tissues moistened with mucus.

Besides the liquids that you drink each day, your body has two additional sources of water. The first is from the fruits and vegetables that you eat and the second is the result of carbohydrate metabolism.

It is interesting to consider that your body is actually about two-thirds water and that an average adult body contains forty to fifty quarts of water with 40 percent of it inside the cells.

When you are thirsty, two mechanisms are involved to produce this important warning signal. When your blood becomes too salty, it draws water from the salivary glands. This dries your mouth and produces the sensation of thirst. Also, the salty blood signals the brain directly that more liquid is needed. Thirst, however, is an imperfect signal because it tends to shut off before you have had enough to satisfy your body's needs. For anyone who is physically active it is imperative to continue drinking beyond the point of quenching thirst.

Examine Your Eating Habits
Put a check mark next to the questions to which you would answer yes.

———— 1.   Do you frequently feel listless after eating?
———— 2.   Do you have a history of indigestion?
———— 3.   Do you have a history of constipation?
———— 4.   Do you have a history of diarrhea?
———— 5.   Do you have a history of excess gas?
———— 6.   Are you overweight?
———— 7.   Do you often have cravings for food you should not eat?
———— 8.   Do you eat a lot of canned or prepared convenience foods?
———— 9.   Do you usually put salt on your food?
————10.   Do you crave sugar and sugary foods?
————11.   Do you often eat high fat, high cholesterol foods?
————12.   Do you eat, chew, and swallow rapidly?
————13.   Do you eat fairly well except that you do not know when to stop?
————14.   Do you frequently skip breakfast?
————15.   Do you often eat while working or "on the run"?
————16.   Do you like to eat late at night?
————17.   Do you usually not bother to read food labels?
————18.   Do you eat a lot of junk food?
————19.   Do you need coffee in the morning to get going?
————20.   When you go too long without eating do you become irritable?

If you have answered positively to ten or more of the questions, your eating habits and food selections may be restricting your energy level.

Your Food Choices
There is a staggering variety of foods to choose from and no two are exactly alike in nutritional value. To avoid having to memorize the nutrient composition of all these foods in order to assess your diet properly, nutritional experts have

devised various systems of grouping foods together. The two most useful kinds of groups are the exchange system and food group systems. We have included both systems because we feel that they are valid ways to make nutritionally sound food choices.

Exchange Systems

In an exchange system, foods are grouped so that their carbohydrate, fat, protein, and calorie contents are similar. For example, a slice of bread is similar to a small potato because both contain about 15 grams of carbohydrate, 2 grams of protein, and negligible fat. Both provide about 70 calories. A slice of bread could be exchanged (traded) for a potato without altering the amount of carbohydrate or protein or the number of calories served. Following are the six exchange groups:

Exchange Group	Serving Size	Carbohydrate Grams	Protein Grams	Fat Grams	Energy (Calories)
Skim milk	1 cup	12	8	0	80
Vegetables	1 cup	5	2	0	25
Fruit	average size	10	0	0	40
Bread	1 slice	15	2	0	70
Lean meat	1 oz	0	7	3	55
Fat	1 tsp	0	0	5	45

We have included the following exchange lists to help you plan your eating program. As you will see, it is easy using the Exchange System, to adjust your calorie levels to your needs. We also suggest that you purchase an inexpensive calorie/gram counter as a further aid.

Milk Group
Milk is a basic food for your diet because of its high nutritional value. It is a major source of calcium and is also rich in many other minerals and vitamins.

One nonfat milk exchange contains:
    Calories 80; Protein 8 g.;
    Carbohydrate 12 g.; Fat 0

One low-fat milk exchange contains:
    Calories 125; Protein 8 g.;
    Carbohydrate 12 g.; Fat 5 g.

Each of the following foods in the amount listed is considered one milk exchange:

NONFAT
Skim or nonfat milk	1 cup
Instant nonfat milk powder	1/3 cup
Undiluted evaporated skim milk	1/2 cup
Buttermilk made from skim milk	1 cup
Hoop cheese	1/2 cup
Egg whites	4 large

LOW-FAT (use in limited amounts)

Low-fat milk	1 cup
Low-fat yogurt	1 cup
Low-fat cottage cheese	1/2 cup

To be avoided:

Whole milk, in any form
Whole milk cheese
Cream (sweet or sour)
Filled milks (which contain coconut oil)
Ice cream
Ice milk
Frozen desserts containing coconut oil
Egg yolk or whole egg
Buttermilk made from whole milk

Meat Group

Meat, fish, and poultry are important sources of protein, iron, and several B vitamins, especially B_{12}. Only those meats which are very lean should be chosen; avoid meat cuts that are marbled or streaked with fat. Remove all visible fat and skin before eating.

One lean meat exchange contains:
Calories 165; Protein 21 g.;
Carbohydrate 0; Fat 9 g.

Three ounces of the following foods, fresh or frozen, is considered one serving:*

Beef—baby beef (very lean), chuck, flank steak, tenderloin, plate ribs, plate
skirt steak, round (bottom, top), rump
Veal—leg, loin, chuck, shank, round rump
Lamb—leg, rib, sirloin, loin (roast and chops), shank, shoulder
Pork—leg (whole rump, center shank)
Poultry—without skin—chicken, turkey, Cornish hen, game birds
Fish—any fresh or frozen, water-packed tuna
Shrimp, crab, lobster, scallops, clams, oysters**

To be avoided:

Fatty meats
Organ meats (liver, heart, kidney, and sweetbreads)
Fried meats

* Three ounces of cooked meat is equal to four ounces raw. Three-fourths cup of cooked meat, poultry, or fish (flaked or chopped) is approximately three ounces.
** Limited amounts because of higher cholesterol content.

Canned meats other than water-packed tuna
Sardines
Luncheon meats
Hamburger
Frankfurters
Sausage
Spare ribs
Pork butt, shoulder, loin
Bacon
Corned beef
Poultry skin
Goose
Duck

Bread/Cereal Group

Whole grain and enriched breads and cereals and dried beans and peas are good sources of iron and some of the B vitamins. Wheat germ, potatoes, lima beans, parsnips, pumpkin, and winter squash are especially high in potassium. Dried beans and peas and whole grain breads and cereals are also excellent sources of fiber.

Starchy vegetables are included in this group because their carbohydrate and protein content is equivalent to that in one slice of bread.

One bread/cereal exchange contains:
Calories 70;   Protein 2 g.;
Carbohydrate 15 g.;   Fat 0

Each of the following foods in the amount listed is considered one bread/cereal exchange:

Whole wheat bread	1 slice
Whole wheat pita bread	1 slice
Whole wheat English muffin	1/2
Bagel	1/2
Corn tortilla	1 (6")
Ready-to-eat unsweetened cereal	3/4 cup
Puffed cereal (unfrosted)*	1 cup
Bran flakes	1/2 cup
Grapenuts	1/4 cup
Wheat germ	1/4 cup
Cooked cereal	1/2 cup
Cooked pasta, spaghetti, macaroni	1/2 cup
Cooked rice	1/2 cup
Popcorn (popped, no fat added)	3 cups

* Varieties low in sodium are shredded wheat, puffed wheat, and puffed rice.

Graham crackers	2 (2 1/2″ squares)
Melba toast	4 rectangles
Rye wafers	3 wafers
Angel food cake	1 1/2″ cube
Beans, peas, and lentils (cooked)	1/2 cup
Corn	1/3 cup
Lima beans	1/2 cup
Green peas	1/2 cup
Potato, white	1 small
Pumpkin	3/4 cup
Winter squash	1/2 cup
Yam or sweet potato	1/4 cup

To be avoided:
  Commercially baked goods (other than bread)
  Brown and serve rolls
  Dinner rolls
  Sweet rolls
  Biscuits
  Muffins
  Hot roll mix
  Prepared cake mix
  Cheese crackers
  Flavored crackers
  Frozen breaded foods
  Frozen French-fried potatoes
  Noodles
  Pork and beans
  Potato chips, corn chips
  Canned refried beans

Vegetable Group

Vegetables are generally high in nutrients, yet low in calories. Dark green and deep yellow vegetables are good sources of vitamin A. Some vegetables which are high in vitamin C are asparagus, broccoli, Brussels sprouts, cabbage, green peppers, greens, and tomatoes. Good sources of potassium are broccoli, Brussels sprouts, greens, and tomatoes. Fiber is present in all vegetables but is especially high in broccoli, Brussels sprouts, beets, cabbage, carrots, eggplant, cauliflower, and beans.

One vegetable exchange contains:
  Calories 25;   Protein 2 g.;
  Carbohydrate 5 g.;   Fat 0

One-half cup of any vegetable cooked is equivalent to one vegetable exchange:

Artichokes	Eggplant	Mushrooms
Asparagus	Green pepper	Okra
Bean sprouts	Greens:	Onions
Beets	Beet	Rhubarb
Broccoli	Chard	Rutabaga
Brussels sprouts	Collard	String beans
Cabbage	Dandelion	Summer squash
Carrots	Kale	Tomatoes
Cauliflower	Mustard	Low sodium tomato juice
Celery	Spinach	Turnips
Cucumbers	Turnip	

The following raw vegetables may be used as desired:

Chicory	Lettuce
Chinese cabbage	Parsley
Endive	Radishes
Escarole	Watercress

Note: Starchy vegetables are found in the Bread/Cereal Group.

To be avoided:
Deep-fried vegetables
Vegetables frozen "with added salt" or in sauces and butter
Breaded vegetables
Canned vegetables
Sauerkraut

Fruit Group

Fruits are good sources of vitamins and minerals. Peaches, cantaloupe, apricots, nectarines, watermelon, and prunes are good sources of vitamin A. Citrus fruits (oranges and grapefruits) and fresh fruit juices, strawberries, and watermelon are excellent sources of vitamin C. Bananas provide abundant amounts of potassium, an important mineral that is needed for proper muscle function. Dried fruits, raisins, dates, prunes, and apricots are good sources of iron. Fruits are also good sources of starch and natural sugars. The fiber and water content of fruits add bulk and volume to your diet. A type of fiber called *pectin* that is especially found in apples can aid the elimination process and help to lower blood levels of cholesterol. Fruits can satisfy that end-of-the-meal sweet craving in a nutritious nonfattening way.

One fruit exchange contains:
Calories 40;   Protein 0;
Carbohydrate 10;   Fat 0

Each of the following fruits in the amount listed is considered one fruit exchange.

Apple, raw	1/2 medium	Nectarine	1 medium
Apricots, raw	2	Orange	1 medium
Banana	1/2 (6″)	Peach	1 medium
Blackberries	1/3 cup	Pear	1 small
Blueberries	1/2 cup	Pineapple	1/2 cup cubes
Cantaloupe	1/2 (5″)	Plums	2 medium
Cherries	10 large	Prunes, cooked	2
Cherries, canned	1/3 cup+2	Raisins	2 tablespoons
Crab apple	1	Raspberries	1/2 cup
Dates	2	Rhubarb, cooked	1 cup
Fig, dried	1	Strawberries	1 cup
Gooseberries	3/4 cup	Tangerine	1
Grapefruit	1/2 small	Watermelon	5″ triangle (1″ thick)
Grapes	14	Honeydew	1/2 (5″ slice)

Fat Group

Fats are either of animal or vegetable origin, or a combination of the two. Fats which remain liquid at room temperature are of vegetable origin and are usually polyunsaturated. Those which are "hard" are generally saturated and of animal origin. In between are combinations ranging from soft margarines, whose main ingredient is vegetable oil and which are therefore predominantly polyunsaturated, to vegetable shortenings which are primarily saturated. Only those fats which are predominantly polyunsaturated should be used.

One fat exchange contains:
Calories 45;   Protein 0;
Carbohydrate 0;   Fat 5 g.

Each of the following foods in the amount listed is considered one fat exchange:

Vegetable oil margarine	1 teaspoon
Vegetable oil (corn, cottonseed, soybean, safflower, sunflower)	1 teaspoon
Peanut butter	2 teaspoons
French or Italian dressing	1 tablespoon
Coarsely chopped nuts, unsalted	1 tablespoon
Avocado	1/8
Mayonnaise	1 teaspoon

To be avoided:

Butter and products containing butter
Margarines and shortenings which are primarily hydrogenated

Animal fats, including lard, bacon fat, and meat drippings, and products
made with them
Chocolate
Coconut
Palm oil, coconut oil

Miscellaneous
Calorie-free items:
The following foods may be used in unlimited amounts:

Tea
Herbs, spices,
Vinegar
Lemon juice
Sugar-free soft drinks (large quantities will add some sodium to diet)

The Basic Four Food Plan

A very practical way of planning for a nutritionally adequate diet which will ensure
a high level of energy, is to balance your intake throughout the entire day. The
Basic Four Food Plan is a guide which outlines your daily nutritional needs. The
guide consists of four food groups and recommended servings in each group. Each
group fulfills a specific nutritional need. The Basic Four Plan was designed by the
Council on Food and Nutrition of the American Medical Association and found
to be consistent with current authoritative medical opinion.
   In this plan food is grouped as follows:

Meat and substitutes for meat
   Sample foods: Beef, pork, lamb, fish, poultry, eggs, nuts, and legumes
   Main nutrient contributions: Protein, iron, riboflavin, niacin, and thiamine
   Recommended daily servings: Two 3 ounce servings

This group supplies about one-half of the protein recommended daily for good
nutrition. Eggs and meat, especially liver, are important sources of iron and the
B vitamins. Pork supplies large amounts of thiamine. Various types of meat differ
in the percentage of fat per pound therefore it is advisable to trim off all excess
fat from prepared meats and also restrict the meats which are higher in fat content
to occasional use.

Milk products
   Sample foods: Milk, buttermilk, yogurt, cheese, cottage cheese, soy milk,
      ice cream
   Main nutrient contributions: Calcium, protein, riboflavin, thiamine
   Recommended daily servings: Two cups for adults

The recommended quantities of milk fulfill about three-fourths of your daily calcium needs. Milk, cheese, and yogurt also contribute high quality protein and vitamins (especially vitamins D and A).

Bread and cereals
    Sample foods: All whole-grain and enriched flours and products, beans and nuts
    Main nutrient contributions: Riboflavin, niacin, iron, thiamine
    Recommended daily servings: Four servings

This group is rich in valuable amounts of several B vitamins. Within this group, the most nutritious grains are the whole grains. These contain from 7 to 14 percent protein and 75 percent carbohydrate, making them an excellent energy source.

Fruits and vegetables
    Sample foods: All fruits and vegetables
    Main nutrient contributions: Vitamins A and C, thiamine, iron and riboflavin
    Recommended daily servings: Four servings

Fruits and vegetables provide needed roughage in addition to nutrients they supply. Those that are used soon after picking have a higher vitamin and mineral content than those that are stored or processed. Fresh fruit or vegetable juices can also be an excellent source of vitamins and minerals.

This balanced food plan is low in calories. If eaten in the quantities suggested, it contains about 1,200 calories per day. Added snacks, condiments, and fat servings add extra calories. If you have a moderate to large energy output each day then you should add additional servings from each of the four categories.

It is also possible to use this plan in conjunction with the exchange system. If you wish to be certain to include all the nutrients but limit consumption of excess calories at the same time you might use the Basic Four Group Plan as a guide. This will enable you to select the proper amount of nutrients. You could then use the exchange lists to choose the actual items.

Four Food Group Plan	Exchange System	Example	Calories
Milk	Milk	2 cups skim milk	160
2 servings	2 exchanges		
Meat	Meat	5 oz. meat	265
2 servings	5 exchanges		
Fruit and vegetable	Fruit and vegetable	2 vegetables	70
2 servings	4 exchanges	2 fruits	80
Bread and cereal	Bread	4 bread slices	280
4 servings	4 exchanges		

For additional information we suggest that you write to the Printing Office,

Superintendent of Documents, Washington, D.C. for a copy of *Ideas for Better Eating*.

The Basic Four Food Plan, Modified

The Center for Science in the Public Interest has devised a modification of the Basic Four Food Plan that places more emphasis on foods that are lower in fat, cholesterol, salt, and added starches. CSPI's program provides an excellent way to make sensible selections within the framework of the Basic Four Food Plan. The chart that follows will help you by giving you specific guidelines within the overall concept of the Basic Four Food Plan.

Anytime	*In moderation*	*Now and then*
BEANS, GRAINS, AND NUTS (4 or more servings per day)		
Bread and rolls (whole grain)	Corn bread [8]	Croissant[4,8]
Bulgur	Flour tortilla[8]	Doughnut[3] or [4,5,8]
Dried beans and peas	Granola cereals[1] or [2]	Presweetened cereals[5,8]
Lentils	Hominy grits[8]	Sticky buns[1] or [2,5,8]
Oatmeal	Macaroni and cheese[1,(6),8]	Stuffing (with butter)[4,(6),8]
Pasta, whole wheat	Matzoh[8]	
Rice, brown	Nuts[3]	
Sprouts	Pastas, refined[8]	
Whole-grain hot and cold cereals	Peanut butter[3]	
Whole wheat matzoh	Pizza[6,8]	
	Refined, unsweetened cereals[8]	
	Refried beans[1] or [2]	
	Seeds[3]	
	Soybeans[2]	
	Tofu[2]	
	Waffles or pancakes with syrup[5,(6),8]	
	White bread and rolls[8]	
	White rice[8]	
FRUITS AND VEGETABLES (4 or more servings per day)		
All fruits and vegetables except those at right	Avocado[3]	Coconut[4]
Applesauce (unsweetened)	Cole slaw[5]	Pickles[6]
Unsweetened fruit juices	Cranberry sauce[5]	
Unsalted vegetable juices	Dried fruit	
Potatoes, white or sweet	French fries[1] or [2]	
	Fried eggplant[2]	
	Fruits canned in syrup[5]	
	Gazpacho[2,(6)]	
	Glazed carrots[5,(6)]	
	Guacamole[3]	
	Potatoes au gratin[1,(6)]	
	Salted vegetable juices[6]	
	Sweetened fruit juices[5]	
	Vegetables canned with salt[6]	

Anytime	In moderation	Now and then
	MILK PRODUCTS	
	(3 to 4 servings per day for children, 2 for adults)	
Buttermilk (from skim milk)	Cocoa with skim milk[5]	Cheesecake[4,5]
Low-fat cottage cheese	Cottage cheese, regular[1]	Cheese fondue[4,(6)]
	Frozen yogurt[5]	Cheese souffle[4,(6),7]
Low-fat milk (1%)	Ice milk[5]	Eggnog[1,5,7]
Low-fat yogurt	Low-fat milk (2%)[1]	Hard cheeses: blue, brick
Nonfat dry milk	Low-fat yogurt, sweetened[5]	Camembert, cheddar,
Skim milk cheeses	Mozzarella, part-milk[1,(6)]	Swiss, Muenster[4,(6)]
Skim milk		Ice cream[4,5]
Skim milk and banana shake		Processed cheeses[4,6]
		Whole milk[4]
		Whole milk yogurt[4]
	POULTRY, FISH, MEAT, AND EGGS	
	(2 servings per day; vegetarians should eat added servings from other groups)	
Cod	Fried fish[1] or [2]	Fried chicken, commercial[4]
Flounder	Herring[3,6]	Cheese omelet[4,7]
Gefilte fish	Mackerel, canned[2,(6)]	Whole egg or yolk
Haddock	Salmon, canned[2,(6)]	(Limit to 3 a week)[3,7]
Halibut	Sardines[2,(6)]	Bacon[4,(6)]
Perch	Shrimp[7]	Beef liver, fried[1,7]
Pollock	Tuna, oil-packed[2,(6)]	Bologna[4,6]
Rockfish	Chicken liver[7]	Corned beef[4,6]
Shellfish, except shrimp	Fried chicken in vegetable oil (homemade)[3]	Ground beef[4]
Sole	Chicken or turkey, boiled, baked, roasted (with skin)[2]	Ham, trimmed[1,6]
Tuna, water-packed	Flank steak[1]	Hot dogs[4,6]
Egg whites	Leg or loin of lamb[1]	Liverwurst[4,6]
Chicken or turkey, boiled, baked, or roasted (no skin)	Pork shoulder or loin, lean[1]	Pig's feet[4]
	Round steak or ground round[1]	Salami[4,6]
	Rump roast[1]	Sausage[4,6]
	Sirloin steak, lean[1]	Spareribs[4]
	Veal[1]	Red meats, untrimmed[4]

Source: Developed by the Center for Science in the Public Interest

[1]Moderate fat, saturated.   [4]High fat, saturated.   [(6)]May be high in salt or sodium.
[2]Moderate fat, unsaturated.   [5]High in added sugar.   [7]High in cholesterol.
[3]High fat, unsaturated.   [6]High in salt or sodium.   [8]Refined grains.

Keeping Track of What You Eat

The following chart is an example of how you can simply keep track of what you eat to ensure the balance of types of foods to fulfill your entire nutritional needs. It charts the number of servings each day for seven days and then averages the number of servings per day for one week. Keeping track of your servings by the week allows for fluctuations in your daily routines.

Fig. 12

Day	Dairy 2 or more servings	Meat 2 or more servings	Cereals and grains 4 or more servings	Fruits and vegetables 4 or more servings	Fats	Snacks
1						
2						
3						
4						
5						
6						
7						
Add all Servings						
Divide by 7						

Dietary Guidelines for Americans

The Human Nutrition Center of the Department of Agriculture (USDA) and the Department of Health, Education, and Welfare (USDHEW) produced a document entitled *Dietary Guidelines for Americans* which includes the seven following guidelines:

1. *Eat a variety of foods daily*. Include these foods everyday: fruits and vegetables; whole grain and enriched breads and cereals; milk and milk products; meat, fish, poultry and eggs, dried peas and beans.
2. *Maintain ideal weight*. Increase physical activity; reduce calories by eating fewer fatty foods and sweets and less sugar, and by avoiding too much alcohol; lose weight gradually.
3. *Avoid too much fat, saturated fat, and cholesterol*. Choose low-fat protein sources such as lean meat, fish, poultry, dry peas and beans; use eggs and organ meats in moderation; limit intake of fats on and in foods; trim fats from meat, broil, bake or boil. Do not fry foods. Read food labels for fat contents.
4. *Eat foods with adequate starch and fiber*. Substitute starches for fats and sugars; select whole grain breads and cereal, fruits and vegetables, dried beans and peas, and nuts to increase fiber and starch intake.
5. *Avoid too much sugar*. Use less sugar, syrup, and honey; reduce concentrated sweets like candy, soft drinks, and cookies; select fresh fruits or fruits canned in light syrup or their own juices; read food labels. Sucrose, glucose, dextrose, maltose, lactose, fructose, syrups, and honey are all sugars.
6. *Avoid too much sodium*. Reduce salt in cooking; add little or no salt at the table; limit salty foods like potato chips, pretzels, salted nuts, popcorn, condiments, cheese, pickled foods, and cured meats; read food labels for sodium or salt especially in processed and snack foods.

7. *If you drink alcohol, do so in moderation.* For individuals who drink, limit all alcoholic beverages (including wine, beer, liquors, etc.) to one or two drinks per day.

Non-traditional Eating Plans

In this section we have stressed the Exchange System and the Basic Four Food Plans because they represent the traditional way our society views the subject of nutrition. They are unquestionably excellent sources of nutrition and will serve your best interests without looking further for diet information.

If you are interested in alternate methods and ideas, and would feel comfortable in trying other suggestions, we have included several for your consideration. These are non-traditional ways of *Eating for Energy* that are still centered in the Western concept of nutrition.

We would like to add a word of caution. There are *many* books and magazines which are filled with misleading information. When you decide to attempt a non-traditional approach or alter your eating habits we suggest that you first check with a qualified health professional before you begin any new program.

The best way to get reliable nutrition advice is to find a registered dietitian (R.D.) in your area. A registered dietitian has completed a prescribed course of study in dietetics or nutrition at an accredited college or university, plus an internship in a hospital or other professional setting, or three years of specialized work experience. A R.D. must pass a registration examination and must maintain proficiency through continuing education.

For general nutrition information, there are many reliable sources that supply excellent material at no cost or for just a minimal charge. Among them are local health departments, departments of nutrition at colleges, universities and medical centers. There are also local chapters of the American Heart Association, American Dietetic Association, and the American Diabetes Association.

We have included a list of newsletters and reference books at the end of this book that will help you find the information you need.

You might also consider subscribing to such newsletters as the following: *Nutrition and Health*, prepared and published six times a year by the Institute of Human Nutrition, Columbia University College of Physicians and Surgeons, 701 West 168 Street, New York, New York, 10032; *Environmental Nutrition Newsletter*, prepared by three dietitians and published ten times a year by Environmental Nutrition, Inc., 52 Riverside Drive, Suite 15-A, New York, New York 10024.

For those who are more politically oriented, the following independent "action" newsletters may prove stimulating: *Nutrition Action*, published twelve times a year by the Center for Science in the Public Interest, 1755 S Street NW, Washington, D.C. 20009 (annual subscription fee includes membership in the organization, two nutrition posters, and a 10-percent discount on the center of health's other publications); *CNI Weekly Report*, published five times a year by the Community Nutrition Institute, 1146 Nineteenth Street NW, Washington, D.C. 20036.

The Vegetarian Diet

Many vegetarians claim that they have more energy and a higher degree of health and vitality than they had before adopting this way of eating. Basically, the vegetarian diet concentrates on just two factors: the elimination of all or most flesh products and the consumption of a diet composed largely of plant foods that are correctly combined for a high degree of digestion and assimilation.

The most important question asked about this diet is whether it is adequate to supply all human nutritional requirements. The vegetarian way of eating is completely safe as long as all meal patterns meet the standard of scientific principles of nutrition. If practiced properly, and initially with qualified supervision, it is completely adequate and actually surpasses some less-varied non-vegetarian meal plans.

The claims for abundant health and energy related to vegetarianism must also be seen in the context of the vegetarian lifestyle. Vegetarians are noted for their high degree of health awareness. They exclude excesses of all kind from their diet including processed foods, sugar, coffee, and alcohol. They also are concerned with their environment and usually endeavor to live in harmonious natural surroundings.

Food Combining

Food combining has become a popular way of eating for energy. Advocates of this system claim that a high degree of well-being is experienced when this method of eating is followed with regularity. Simply stated, different foods require different conditions for efficient digestion and assimilation. For example, proteins require the most time and energy to digest. The process which breaks down proteins is different from the process which breaks down carbohydrates. Therefore, when a protein is eaten with a carbohydrate, such as meat and a piece of bread or potato, the different digestive juices modify each other's effectiveness. Foods that are not digested properly spoil in the digestive tract and produce poisons which contribute to illness and fatigue.

Those who practice food combining believe that eating one or two foods that combine well together puts less strain on the digestive process thereby creating fewer toxins to eliminate. They also believe that by adhering to the rules of proper food combining, the digestive system is worked less which conserves energy for use elsewhere in the body.

The preferred food combinations are:
- Proteins combine with green and low starch vegetables.
- Starches also combine with green and low starch vegetables.
- Fruits should be eaten at least one hour before or after any meal because they digest rapidly. When combined with other foods this process is slowed and excess fermentation takes place.

A word of caution: If you are interested in this diet and would like to try it for yourself, the first step to take would be to consult with a nutritionist who is com-

Fig. 13

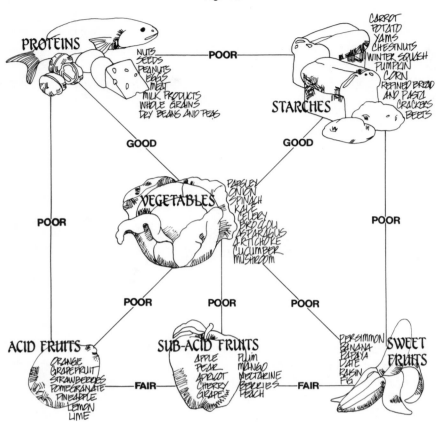

pletely familiar with all aspects of food combining. We have chosen a number of books for your further information and strongly suggest that you fully understand the diet before you attempt to combine your foods.

The Eastern Concept

Over four thousand years ago it was written in *The Yellow Emperor's Classic of Internal Medicine:*

> Those who rebel against the basic rules of the universe sever their own roots and ruin their selves . . . the two principles in nature (expansion and contraction) and the four seasons are the beginning and the end of everything and they are also the cause of life and death. Those who disobey the laws of nature will give rise to calamities and visitations while those who follow the laws of nature remain free from dangerous illness.

In the Eastern traditions the human body is seen to be a microcosm of the universe requiring a balance of yin and yang energy to function properly. Therefore, it is thought that the most nutritious diet consists of simple foods that are balanced and in harmony with their natural sources. Man's body, his food and his immediate surroundings are seen as three interrelated energy forms. Therefore, the energy that food imparts is related not only to its taste and flavor but to the way it is prepared, the quality of its selection, the way it is cut, the length of cooking time, the amount of seasoning, and how the meal is presented at the table.

Cooking is considered to be a very important function in an Eastern household because the cook is responsible for the health and well-being of the family. If the person who prepares the family's food cooks with consideration and care, the members of the family will be filled with energy and vibrant health. He or she also provides an atmosphere that is conducive to enjoyment of the meal. Ideally, there is always a harmonious balance of colors at the table, as well as a variety of tastes. Foods are never served too hot nor too cold; too spicy or too bland. Seasonal changes are also taken into consideration to include freshly grown produce rather than food that has been packaged or processed.

This way of eating has been practiced in the East for thousands of years and is gaining many advocates in the Western world as well. It is called Macrobiotics. Its major focus is on the relationship between humans and the natural world. Those practicing this way are committed currently to a philosophy that is based on reversing the harmful effects of industrialization and urbanization. They believe that the further removed we become from our natural state the more vulnerable we are to sickness and unhappiness, which is nature's way of telling us to adopt a proper diet and way of life.

Macrobiotics

For many centuries there have been advocates of a diet that was said to increase energy and promote health and longevity. It was first documented in classical

Greece in the writings of Hippocrates and Aristotle. The word "macrobiotic" comes from the Greek words *macro* meaning "whole" and *biotic* meaning "way of life."

In every age there have been followers of this simple way of eating who have described its merits. It has been practiced for centuries in Zen Buddhist monasteries where it is called *Syōjin Ryōri* and is thought to increase happiness and well-being.

In the nineteenth century the traditional diet of Japan, which closely follows macrobiotic principles, became the subject of scientific inquiry and shortly thereafter was introduced to the Western world. Its main advocate was George Ohsawa who published over three hundred diet and nutrition books and is credited with the spread of the worldwide popularity of the macrobiotic way of life. Many of his students are currently lecturing and writing about the benefits of macrobiotics.

Yin and Yang—The Macrobiotic Philosophy

- *The Seven Universal Principles of the Infinite Universe*
  1. Everything is a differentiation of one infinity.
  2. Everything changes.
  3. All antagonisms are complementary.
  4. There is nothing identical.
  5. What has a front has a back.
  6. The bigger the front, the bigger the back.
  7. What has a beginning has an end.

The principle of yin and yang is known as the Unifying Principle because it states that antagonistic forces complement and unify each other. Eating a macrobiotic diet, therefore, means eating and living in harmony with nature and with the order of the universe. In macrobiotic philosophy there is nothing but yin and yang in the relative world. All manifestations are seen as a blending of these two opposites and choosing to eat foods that complement each other is considered to be the best way to remain balanced and whole. Eating a diet that is too yin is thought to disperse life-force while foods that are too yang are believed to stifle energy and well-being. It is also felt that either extreme creates disease and unhappiness while foods that contain a relative balance of yin and yang create harmony.

The basic characteristics of a food determine whether it is yin or yang. This takes into account the different factors in the growth and structure of foods.

Characteristics of Yin Foods	*Characteristics of Yang Foods*
Growth in a hot climate or in summer	Growth in a cold climate or in winter
More rapid growth	Slower growth
Foods containing more water	Drier foods
Fruits and leaves	Stems, roots, and seeds
Major growth above the ground	Major growth below the ground
Pungent, sour, sharply sweet, hot, and aromatic foods	Salty, plainly sweet, and bitter foods

The Standard Macrobiotic Diet

The standard macrobiotic diet consists of: 50 to 60 percent whole grains and whole-grain products; 20 to 30 percent vegetables that are of organic quality and are locally grown when possible; 5 to 10 percent beans and sea vegetables; 5 to 10 percent soups; and 5 percent condiments and supplementary foods, beverages, fish, and some desserts. All foods are eaten as close to their natural state as possible. Acceptable supplementary foods include: fish and seafood, using less fatty varieties, seasonal fruits, nuts and seeds, natural beverages and natural seasonings and condiments.

Fig. 14

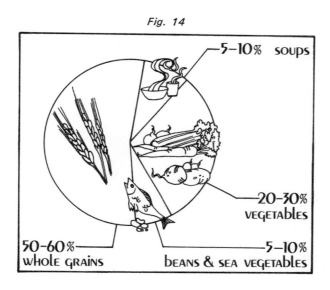

As you can see from the following chart, these foods fall into the middle of the yin/yang category. They are considered to be the most balanced and therefore the highest in energy producing value.

YANG (Contracting Energy)

Strong Yang Foods
 Refined salt
 Eggs
 Meat
 Cheese
 Poultry
 Fatty fish
 Seafood

More Balanced Foods
 Whole cereal grains
 Beans and bean products

Root, round, and leafy green vegetables
Sea vegetables
Unrefined sea salt, vegetable oil, and other seasonings (if moderately used)
Spring water and well water
Non-aromatic, non-stimulant teas and beverages
Seeds and nuts
Temperate climate fruit
Rice syrup, barley malt, and other grain-based natural sweeteners (used in moderation)

YIN (Expanding Energy)

Strong Yin Foods
White rice, white flour
Frozen and canned foods
Tropical fruits and vegetables
Milk, cream, yogurt, and ice cream
Refined oils
Spices (pepper, curry, nutmeg, etc.)
Aromatic and stimulant beverages (coffee, black tea, mint tea, etc.)
Honey, sugar, and refined sweeteners.

Most Western diets combine foods from the strong yang category and the strong yin category. According to the macrobiotic way of eating, food out of harmony with our bodily needs, such as meats, eggs, and hard salty cheeses, which are all yang, stimulate a craving for opposite, or yin foods such as sugar, coffee, alcohol, ice cream, and tropical fruits. The swings from one extreme to the other are said to destroy the body's balance and deplete its energy which in turn leads to illness and fatigue.

The following is a brief description of the types of foods included in a macrobiotic diet. For a more complete understanding of the macrobiotic way of eating, we have included a list of publications for further reading at the end of the book.

Whole Grains

Whole grains comprise 50 to 60 percent of the total volume of each meal. These include brown rice, millet, barley, oats, whole wheat, rye, buckwheat, and corn. These can be eaten with very little preparation or used as flour and grain products in bread and pasta.

Soups

One or two bowls of soup are recommended daily. Soup broth can be made from leftover vegetable water, *miso* or *tamari* soy sauce which are prepared from soybeans, grains, and naturally fermented sea salt. The soup preparation can also include grains, beans, vegetables, fish or seafood. Sea vegetables such as *wakame* or *kombu* make a tasty addition.

Vegetables
About 25 to 30 percent of each meal should include fresh vegetables prepared in a variety of ways.

Beans
Cooked beans or bean products such as *tofu* and *tempeh* comprise about 10 percent of the daily food intake. These can be served individually or cooked together with grains, vegetables or sea vegetables or as the basic ingredient in soup.

Sea Vegetables
Sea vegetables, which are rich in vitamins and minerals, can be included in soups, cooked with vegetables or beans, or prepared as a small side dish.

Salt, Oil, and Seasonings
Unrefined sea salt, miso, tamari soy sauce or *umeboshi* plums are often used in cooking to give a salty taste when desired. Unrefined dark sesame oil is used most often for daily cooking. Light sesame oil, corn oil, and other high quality unrefined vegetable oils are also used. Brown rice vinegar, sweet rice vinegar, and umeboshi vinegar are used for a sour taste. *Kuzu* root powder and arrowroot flour are used for gravies and sauces.

Seafood
White-meat fish contains less fat than red-meat or blue-skinned varieties. Shellfish are also used in moderation. These are often served in soup or lightly cooked.

Seeds and Nuts
Roasted seeds and nuts, sprinkled with sea salt or tamari soy sauce, make delicious snacks. Nut butters can be made with a food processor. They make an excellent dip for vegetables or can be served with bread.

Fruit
Fresh fruits, served in season, make an excellent dessert or snack.

Desserts
Desserts include cookies, puddings, cakes, pies, and other dishes prepared with naturally sweet ingredients or natural sweeteners such as: rice syrup, barley malt, *amazaké*, and apple juice.

The Macrobiotic philosophy includes food for thought as well as food that brings energy and well-being to your body. Those practicing the Macrobiotic Way subscribe to the following *way of life* suggestions:

- Eat slowly and chew your food well.
- Eat only when you are hungry.
- Eat in an orderly and relaxed manner.

- Sit with a good posture at the table and take a moment, inwardly or outwardly, to express gratitude for your food.
- Leave the table feeling satisfied but not full.
- Avoid eating for three hours before sleeping.
- For the deepest and most restful sleep retire before midnight and rise early in the morning.
- Be as active as possible in your daily life.
- If your condition permits, go outdoors in simple clothing.
- Walk barefoot on the beach, grass, or soil whenever possible, this stimulates the energy flow in your body.
- Keep your home environment clean and orderly, especially the areas where food is prepared and served.
- Develop your appreciation for nature.
- Greet everyone you meet with joy.

This table compares the composition of the Standard American Diet, the Dietary Goals recommended by the Senate Select Committee on Nutrition and Human Needs in 1983, and the Standard Macrobiotic Diet. The percentages of each menu represent the proportion of calories from each food group.

Nutrients	Standard American Diet		Dietary Goals		Macrobiotic Diet	
Fats	Saturated	16%	Saturated	10%	Saturated	2%
	Mono-unsaturated	19%	Mono-unsaturated	10%	Mono-unsaturated	8%
	Poly-unsaturated	7%	Poly-unsaturated	10%	Poly-unsaturated	5%
	Much of it is from meat and dairy products, including highly saturated sources such as butter, steak, and hard cheeses; some highly saturated oils (coconut, palm kernel).		Animal sources with less saturated fat, i.e., margarine instead of butter; lean meat; low-fat dairy		Primary sources of fat are from whole grains and beans, vegetable oils such as sesame used in cooking, seeds and nuts.	
Proteins	Animal sources	8%	Poultry and fish	8%	Plant sources	8%
	Other sources	4%	Lean meat and other	4%	Fish and other	4%
	Mostly from animal sources such as meat, eggs, and dairy products		Poultry, fish, lean meat, low-fat dairy products, beans, nuts		Plant sources such as tofu and tempeh, and some fish, seeds, and nuts	
Carbohy-drates	Refined flour	28%	Fresh vegetables, fruit, and whole grains	48%	Whole grain, fresh vegetables, sea vegetables, fruits, some naturally occurring sugars	73%
	Refined and processed sugars	18%	Refined and processed sugars	10%		
	White bread, processed cereals, pastries, sugared beverages, ice cream, French fries, donuts, potato chips, some canned and frozen fruits and vegetables, alcohol		Refined cereal products; whole grains and whole grain flours; honey, cane and beet sugar, molasses		Primarily from whole grains such as brown rice, barley, rye, millet, buckwheat, corn, whole wheat, fresh vegetables, sea vegetables, and some fruit	

Breathing

The Western Concept

To Breathe Is to Live

Every moment of every day your energy level is affected by the quality of your breathing as well as the quality of the air you breathe. However, since breathing is most often an involuntary response, you have probably given very little attention to it and yet you cannot live without it. You can survive for some time without eating, a shorter time without drinking, but without air, life will cease within a matter of minutes.

Every cell in your body "breathes" and requires a constant supply of oxygen to carry out its assigned function. Therefore, it is of interest to consider the following:

- On the average, you breathe sixteen times every minute.
- If the air cells of your lungs were spread out over an unbroken surface, they would cover a surface of 14,000 square feet.
- Every twenty four hours approximately 35,000 pints of blood traverse the capillaries of your lungs.

When the air is clear and your lungs are strong, your breathing produces a feeling of high energy and well-being. Unfortunately, for those of us living in large cities, this ideal can be difficult to achieve. Automobiles, aside from the tension caused by driving them and the fumes they emit, are rarely designed to allow a relaxed sitting posture which is vital for natural breathing. Working at a standard office desk means leaning forward for hours placing a strain on neck and back muscles which in turn hampers breathing. The same problems exist for those who must frequently talk on the telephone.

Also, clothing design may discourage freedom of movement and restrict breathing. Our culture prizes a flat belly and continues to invent a variety of torturous ways of assuring it such as figure-controlling panty hose, all-day girdles, and tight fitting jeans. Along with all of these can be added the further restrictions of smoking, ill health, poorly functioning organs, and muscle tension created by emotions such as fear, anger, and anxiety.

Your body responds to these abuses by breathing from the upper chest with shallow breaths which means that on the average, your lungs are only partially filled with oxygen. This is in contrast to the habit of natural, full breathing demonstrated by healthy children, animals, and primitive peoples.

Fortunately there are many ways to make certain that your lungs are working to their fullest, providing you with abundant vitality and energy.

The first step is to become completely aware of the breathing restrictions in your life. You must also become aware of the need for changes in your breathing habits and make some constructive decisions which will help to undo the damage already inflicted. These steps can be brought about more readily once you have a clearer understanding of this remarkably adaptive and resilient system.

The Process of Breathing

Breathing may be likened to the functioning of an old-fashioned blacksmith's bellows. When the handles are lifted, the bellows open and air is sucked in. When the handles are pressed down the bellows flatten and the air rushes out.

A number of muscles make up the bellows within your body. The most active of these is the diaphragm, a dome shaped muscle located at the base of your rib cage and above your stomach. The diaphragm's action is almost as automatic as that of the heart, although it may be transformed into a semi-voluntary muscle by an effort of the will.

The diaphragm contracts during inhalation and pulls down on the bottom of your chest, increasing the volume inside your chest cavity. At the same time, chest capacity can be further increased by elevating your ribs slightly and moving them outward and upward. Air rushes into the vacuum thus created. When the diaphragm relaxes the chest and lungs contract and the air is expelled.

The Organs of Respiration

The organs of respiration consist of the lungs and all the passages leading to them. The lungs occupy the pleural chamber of the thorax, one on each side of the median line and separated from each other by the heart, the greater blood vessels, and the larger air tubes. Each lung is free in all directions except at the root, which consists chiefly of the bronchi, arteries, and veins connecting the lungs with the trachea and heart. The lungs are spongy and porous, and their tissues are very elastic. They are covered with a delicately constructed but strong sac, known as the pleural sac, one wall of which closely adheres to the lung, and the other to the inner wall of the chest. A fluid is secreted in this area which allows the inner surfaces of the walls to glide easily upon each other in the act of breathing.

The air passages consist of the interior of the nose, pharynx, larynx, windpipe or trachea, and the bronchial tubes. When you breathe, you draw air in through your nose, where it is warmed by contact with the mucous membrane, which is richly supplied with blood. After it has passed through the pharynx and larynx it passes into the trachea, which subdivides into numerous tubes called *bronchia*, these in turn subdivide into and terminate in the lungs in millions of minute subdivisions consisting of air sacs called *alveoli*. As blood passes through your lungs it comes into contact with the air sacs which function to exchange waste products for oxygen.

Blood is driven by the heart, through the arteries, into the capillaries, thus reaching every part of the body. It then returns through another route by means of the capillaries and veins, to the heart, and is once again drawn into the lungs.

The blood begins its arterial journey, bright red and rich, laden with life-giving oxygen. It returns by the venous route dull in color and filled with waste products. This stream goes to the right auricle of the heart. When the auricle becomes filled with venous blood, it contracts and forces the stream of blood through an opening in the right ventricle of the heart, which in turn sends it on to the lungs. There it is distributed by millions of hair-like blood vessels to the air cells of the lungs.

As the venous blood is distributed among the sacs, a breath of air is inhaled and the oxygen of the air comes in contact with the impure blood through the thin walls of hair-like blood vessels. Their walls are thick enough to hold the blood, but thin enough to allow the oxygen to penetrate them. When the oxygen comes in contact with the blood, a form of combustion takes place, and the blood takes up oxygen and releases carbon dioxide which has been generated from the waste products. The blood thus purified and oxygenated, then is carried back to the heart, again rich, red, and laden with life-giving qualities.

Fig. 15

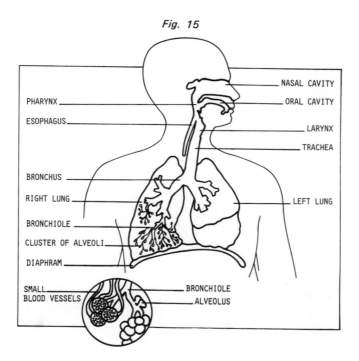

Upon reaching the left auricle of the heart, it is forced into the left ventricle, from where it is again forced out through the arteries on its mission of life and energy to all parts of the system.

The blood system supplies the cells of the body with oxygen and nutrients, and carries away waste materials.

The heart is the vital center of this, being the pump that drives blood through the body. It weighs under a pound, measures on average about 5 inches long by 3 1/2 inches wide, and comprises four, muscular chambers.

The heart is positioned under the rib cage and in front of the lungs. It lies on the center line of the body, but not symmetrically: one end slants out to a point

Fig. 16

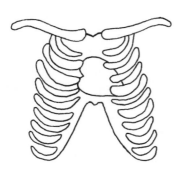
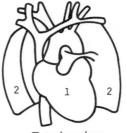
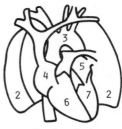

Exterior view   Sectional view

1—Heart   5—Left atrium
2—Lungs   6—Right ventricle
3—Aorta   7—Left ventricle
4—Right atrium

just to the left of the breastbone (sternum). The heartbeat is most noticeable here, giving the impression that the heart lies on the left side of the body.

Tools for Better Breathing

There are a number of ways you can improve the quality of your breathing. (Each of the specific suggestions here will be detailed fully in other sections of the book.)

Aerobic Exercise
The means of evaluating physical fitness have grown in sophistication within the past ten years and it is now an established fact that frequent aerobic exercise encourages deeper and richer breathing. Whether you are swimming, dancing, skiing, walking or running, the amount of oxygen you are able to take in will determine how long you will be able to "endure" in these activities which have been proven to strengthen the heart, lungs, and circulatory system.

Biofeedback
Another tool has recently come into wide usage and acceptance. It is called *biofeedback*. This is the process of becoming aware of physiological events you normally are not aware of with the possibility of gaining voluntary control of such events. Biofeedback is an acronym for biological feedback. Its main purpose is to provide a means for receiving feedback on areas previously labeled involuntary: especially the brain, the heart, and the circulatory system.

Using sophisticated instrumentation, it is now possible to get in touch with the stresses and tensions that impair the body's systems and to focus on the benefits of slow, rhythmic breathing.

Stress Reduction

Currently it is possible to find numerous books and magazine articles devoted to the field of stress management. Foremost among the stress reduction techniques are controlled breathing exercises that bring about a state of peace and calm. We have included several in this section for you to try for yourself.

Guided Imagery

Guided or directed imagery is another well-established technique that can be used to enhance your breathing practice. There are many classes and books available that will introduce you to this type of experience. Those conversant with this technique have reported many positive results including expanded breathing capacity and a feeling of energy and vitality during and after their practice. You might enjoy experimenting with the short guided imagery experience given in this chapter.

Meditation

In meditation a focus on the breath is usually one of the first things taught a beginning student.

By sitting calmly and allowing the breathing to become slow and relaxed the meditator can bring about a state of heightened awareness that produces a feeling of calmness and centeredness.

Environment and Air Quality

Environment also plays a large part in the quality of the air you breathe. If you live or work in a temperature controlled building, experts are now suggesting that you purchase a selection of green plants. The breathing process of plants is opposite to that of man. Plants breathe the carbon dioxide within their environment and give off oxygen. Therefore, they make a healthy addition to any room. Since spending time in natural surroundings is healthy for your respiratory system, having plants in your home or office can help to offset the stuffiness and dryness of the usual modern environment.

Another interesting device has lately become very much in demand. In our technical society it is small wonder that man has created a device to electrically charge the air, creating the same ion environment found after a thunderstorm or near large bodies of water. Air that is close to moving water of any kind is charged with negative ions. These aid the breathing process by clearing the air of pollutants and the larger positive ions which attract smoke, odor, and dust. Negative ion machines have become relatively inexpensive and having one in the sleeping area is thought to promote wholesome and restful sleep.

Breathing Exercises

We recommend the following exercises as an introduction to becoming more in touch with your breathing. With just a little practice you will discover how much more energy is available to you when your breathing capacity is increased.

For the best results, most of these exercises should be practiced in a comfortable place where you will not be disturbed.

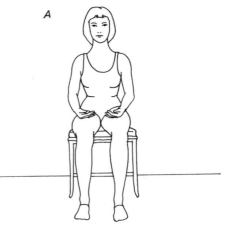

Fig. 17

A

The Natural Breath
1. Lie on your back or sit comfortably and place your hands on your stomach (abdomen).
2. Inhale slowly and deeply through your nose, letting your abdomen expand like a balloon. (Keep your hands on your stomach. You will feel the expansion of this breath.)
3. Let your abdomen relax as you exhale slowly; you are releasing old, stale air.

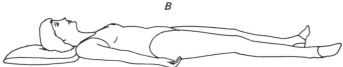

B

4. Inhale easily and slowly. Feel your stomach expand again.
5. Exhale, slowly.

This is the breath that small children and animals use naturally. It is the breath that we must become reacquainted with for health and vitality. Practice this breath as often as you wish.

The Relaxing Breath
1. Do five or more Natural Breaths.
2. Continue the Natural Breaths as you imagine that with each inhalation you are breathing into a tense or a painful part of your body.
3. Imagine tension streaming out of your nostrils with each exhalation. Feel the relaxation in your entire body.
4. Continue this breathing pattern and imagining for as long as you wish.

When breathing for relaxation, it is best to employ a lengthy exhalation. If you find it helpful to breathe with a count, begin with inhalations and exhalations of equal duration (count to four). Change to a count of four in and eight out. With the longer exhalation you will begin to feel relaxed all over.

The Wake-up Your Body Breath
1. Lie on your back in bed. Inhale through your nose and raise your arms perpendicular to the bed.
2. Exhale through your mouth while letting your arms drop.

3. Repeat steps *1* and *2* slowly six times.
4. Inhale deeply and hold your breath ten or fifteen seconds.
5. Exhale forcefully while pulling your stomach in, then sit up.
6. Inhale and reach straight up while sitting.
7. Exhale, pulling your hands down to your shoulders and make a fist with each hand.
8. Repeat steps *6* and *7* several times.
9. As you get out of bed feel how energized and ready for the day you have become.

A Breathing-Walking Combination

Take a brisk walk. Enjoy the scenery and the feeling of exhilaration that you will experience. While walking, add this breathing pattern:
1. Inhale through your nose for four steps while walking. Expand your chest as much as you can.
2. Exhale for eight steps, pulling your stomach in.
3. Allow your back to straighten, stand tall but slightly flex your knees as you walk.
4. Imagine that you feel tension draining out of your neck and back as you exhale.
5. Feel the strength and rhythm of your step. Swing arms freely.
6. Inhale deeply at the conclusion of your walk and let out a large sigh, releasing all tensions. Inhale and sigh several times.

This breathing-walking combination can be used when you have just a short time to exercise or for longer walks. The increase in your energy level will become readily apparent the first time you try it.

The Stress-break Breath

When you have been working hard and are under tension you can take a mini-vacation no matter where you are. It is preferable to sit down for this breath. Uncross your legs and get as comfortable as you can. Sit up straight and let your head roll round several times in both directions.

1. Take slow, deep breaths.
2. Allow your abdomen to fill up completely with oxygen, as you inhale through your nose.
3. Exhale slowly.
4. Continue breathing in this manner for several breaths.
5. Mentally scan your body. Scan slowly from your head to your toes, part by part, area by area. Note the spots that are tense. Focus your breath directly into those spots. You may want to move those areas a little. Move your neck, your shoulders, wiggle your toes.
6. Feel the aches and pains, the stiffness and tensions release and drain away as you exhale.

7. Experience these areas relaxing and opening with oxygen and increased circulation as you inhale.

8. You will discover that this exercise will enable you to go back to whatever you were doing with renewed vigor in mind and body.

A Guided Imagery Breathing Experience

This is a short guided imagery experience. The more you practice it, the more energy you will have.

Get into a comfortable position either sitting or lying down. Uncross your legs and take a slow deep breath. Gently close your eyes.

Bring your attention to your nose and imagine what air looks like as it enters. You might imagine a color or a sound, or see a shape like a cloud or millions of bright lights. Follow its path down into your lungs, observe it swirling around and see it moving back up and out. As it leaves, tell yourself that it is carrying away all of your tensions and anxieties.

Do this for about one to two minutes.

Bring your awareness to the center of your stomach. Again, imagine the oxygen coming in, swirling around your abdomen, lower back, and stomach, slowly watch it leave as you gently exhale.

As you inhale again, draw air into your chest, upper body, and into your heart. Watch it swirling around, carrying away tension as it departs.

Repeat the same process in other areas, especially to those areas which are tense or tight or in pain.

To conclude, breathe naturally, stretch, and slowly open your eyes.

Breathing Breaks

Throughout your day you can stop whatever you are doing for just one or two minutes and *breathe* deeply and fully. You will be amazed at how different you will feel at the end of a day when you have incorporated lots of deep breaths into your daily routine.

If you find that you have difficulty remembering to take large expansive breaths throughout your day, you can use this simple exercise to remind yourself to take a "breathing break."

Purchase a supply of self-adhesive, colored dots at a stationery store. Go through your home and workplace and place these dots in prime locations. Each time you see one, use it as a cue to remind yourself to stop and take several deep breaths. The overall result will be to repeatedly oxygenate your blood. Sooner than you realize the habit of taking "breathing breaks" will become second nature.

The Eastern Concept

The Lungs and Kidneys

In the Eastern traditions the lungs are called "the tender organ" because they are easily influenced by external conditions. The lungs are thought to regulate the Ki of your entire body since they control respiration and are the place where the external Ki meets the Ki inside your body. When your lungs are healthy, Ki enters and leaves smoothly and respiration is even and regular. When inhalation or exhalation is impaired, imbalances can occur throughout your entire system.

The lungs are also seen to rule the exterior of your body because their health is mirrored in healthy skin and body hair. Your lungs open into your nose which is said to be "the thoroughfare for respiration" while the throat is known as "the door of the lungs and the home of the vocal cords." Many common nose and throat disorders are therefore thought to occur when the lung Ki is weak.

Lung energy and kidney energy are also seen to be closely connected. There are many Oriental deep breathing exercises used to charge the lungs and kidneys with Ki because, by insuring efficient elimination of carbon dioxide through the lungs, the less the kidneys will have to eliminate. When carbon dioxide is not released through the lungs it is chemically changed to carbonic acid which must be filtered by the kidneys. This action uses energy and drains Ki from your other body systems.

Breathing at the Cellular Level

Every one of your cells is affected by the quality of your breath. When you are active you become hungry. The cells in your body react in the same way. The more work they do, the more food they need. Every time cells work, oxidation takes place. In this process electrical sparks are generated and thus currents of electricity are sent to all parts of your body. The Eastern texts describe this process as the foundation of Ki. The end product or residue of oxidation is the waste product carbon dioxide. If you picture fuel burning and throwing off ashes you will have an indication of how this process works. Just as a fire cannot burn without oxygen for combustion, your cells cannot burn their nutrients without oxidation. When the spark of Ki activates the potential or stored energy within each of your cells, your body is then able to move and remain warm as one-third of the energy production results in action while the other two-thirds becomes heat energy.

You are composed of many different kinds of cells; bone cells, muscle cells, tissue cells, glandular cells, nerve cells, blood cells, and brain cells. All of these must constantly have the proper combination of nourishment or they will not survive.

They must have protein, carbohydrates, fatty acids, and oxygen so that they can carry out their functions of body repair, heat production, and activity of the mind and body. When you feel tired or fatigued the main cause is that your cells are unable to get all the nourishment they need.

The Lymphatic System

Your blood flows through a series of arteries and veins, each set becoming successively finer in structure. As they diminish in size they are known as venules, arterioles, and capillaries. Their role is to carry nourishment to the cells and receive their waste products for elimination. This is achieved by the action of the lymphatic system. Lymph is a salty, colorless fluid which passes through your body alongside the blood vessels. Its purpose is to bathe the cells with nutrients and to collect the cells' waste products which it delivers back into the bloodstream.

Your body is continually circulating blood and lymph. There are ducts in the thoracic or chest cavity where the lymph is drawn in during inhalation and is pushed away to all other parts of your body in exhalation. The squeezing action produced when your muscles contract also aids the lymphatic flow throughout your body.

Smooth and Rhythmic Breathing

The acidity level of your blood determines your rate of breathing. The waste product, carbon dioxide, builds up in your blood and causes acidity. This, in turn, releases hydrogen ions which excite the nerves in the respiratory center.

There are two sets of nerves which run from the neck to the thoracic cavity and diaphragm. When the carbon dioxide ratio increases, the nerves signal the chest to inhale and the diaphragm to move down. When a sufficient amount of oxygen has entered your lungs the nerves signal that fact to your chest cavity which deflates and causes you to breathe out.

When you are engaged in physical activity more carbon is generated in your body and more hydrogen is released. This causes an increased activity within your respiratory center as you are inhaling and exhaling rapidly to keep up with your energy requirement. If you hold your breath during activity, you are holding in an excess of carbon dioxide which registers in all parts of the body.

At the base of the skull and extending into your neck is a vital nerve center called the *medulla oblongata*. The Eastern term for this center is "the vital knot." From this knot there are two sets of nerves that send branches to the walls of your blood vessels and all of your internal organs. The vasoconstrictor set of nerves cause a constriction or contraction of your blood vessels. The vasodilator set of nerves cause dilation or enlargement of the blood vessels.

Whenever you hold your breath more carbon dioxide is allowed to build up which causes constriction in different parts of your body due to the action of the vasoconstrictor nerves. This acts like a brake to your entire system. To insure a smoothly functioning energy level, the Ki within your body must have an even flow of oxygen, carbon dioxide, blood, and lymph. Spasmodic breathing causes your body to experience extreme stops and starts which, over time, seriously depletes your store of Ki.

Conversely, when smooth and rhythmic breathing becomes a habit, it generates a feeling of high energy and well-being, promoting deep relaxation and sound sleep. This type of breathing also aids digestion and elimination and rejuvenates your entire body.

The Breathing Process

The nitrogen ion in each cell is the catalyst that allows oxidation to take place. It is like nitrogen in a nitroglycerine bomb. When it explodes, the cell is able to exchange waste for the oxygen it needs. When functioning smoothly, this process provides a feeling of vitality and enthusiasm.

However, this system can easily be thrown off balance. By harboring negative emotions such as hate, anger, fear, anxiety, depression, and grief, the constriction and interrupted breathing that accompanies these emotions makes it impossible for the cells to receive enough oxygen and a complete supply of nutrients. This, in turn, produces fatigue and lowered energy levels.

You can easily check to see whether you are experiencing tension and anxiety by checking to see if your neck and shoulder muscles feel tense and tight. If they do, breathe deeply and slowly and release the negative thoughts which are causing tension in your head, neck, and shoulders. When you are carrying excess tension you will also notice, as you are dropping the load from your neck and shoulders, that your breath easily becomes smooth and flowing again.

Eastern sages tell us that there are two yardsticks with which to discover whether or not you are bringing health and abundant Ki to your life. If your breath flows easily and smoothly you are considered to have a smooth and balanced life, filled with health and energy. Conversely, if you habitually encourage jerky and spasmodic breathing you will eventually become devitalized and experience a depletion of your natural vitality.

According to this system of thought, when the flow of blood and lymph is not constricted by tension, the flow of life becomes smooth and effortless. Perfect breathing, whether fast or slow, should be regular and filled with an abundance of Ki.

There are many Eastern systems that teach a wealth of breathing techniques. We will now introduce you to several of them.

Qigong

Qigong (pronounced Cheekung) is a Chinese term applied to many forms of exercise which are designed to raise one's Ki. We will go into further detail in Chapter 4. The word "Qigong" encompasses a broad range of systems, one of which is called Diaoxi (pronounced Diaoshi) or "the principle of breath control."

The first rule of Diaoxi is that breathing must remain natural and unstrained. Instead of inhaling quickly or forcefully, the exercises place an emphasis on the short pause which comes naturally and effortlessly after each inhalation and exhalation. During the momentary pause between each breath, your attention is directed to your lower abdomen. When you do these exercises it is important that you continue to breathe naturally without trying to extend the pause by holding your breath. Breath holding, as we have just indicated, causes constriction and tightness. It is helpful to visualize your breath being drawn down into your lower abdomen. This is what is known in Qigong as the "Ki penetrating breath." The sensation of energy filling your lower abdomen will be tentative and fleeting in the beginning but with continued practice your reward will be smooth, rhythmic, and vital breathing.

To begin your practice of Diaoxi it is important to follow these guidelines:

- Set aside ten or fifteen minutes for your practice.
- Practice regularly for the most benefit.
- Be sure that you will not be disturbed.
- Your clothing should be loose and comfortable.
- Remove glasses, jewelry, tight belts, and shoes.
- Wait an hour or longer after you have eaten before starting your practice.
- Choose a location that is comfortable and well ventilated. You may practice sitting or lying down.

The Basic Principles for Practicing Diaoxi

The first principle of Diaoxi is to relax completely.

Take some slow preparatory breaths and feel the tension draining away.

Assume a comfortable position that is suitable for your practice.

When you have completed your breathing exercises avoid the temptation to jump up and immediately start moving about. Instead, stretch, slowly open your eyes, gently massage your forehead, cheeks, chin, and the back of your neck.

Stand upright and raise up onto your toes several times to get the blood circulating smoothly.

The Soft Breathing Technique

Close your mouth and lightly touch the tip of your tongue to the roof of your mouth.

1. Slowly inhale through your nose and imagine that your breath is being drawn down into your lower abdomen. Your lower abdomen should fill out naturally in this process.
2. Let your tongue down and open your mouth slightly and exhale slowly. You can exhale through your nose and your mouth at the same time if you wish. Your lower abdomen should go in naturally.
3. After exhaling completely, let your breathing pause briefly in a natural way. Leave your tongue down and your mouth slightly open. Your abdomen should also remain slightly collapsed.
4. Continue this breathing pattern for several minutes.

This breathing technique will calm your entire system and will restore your energy when you are feeling tired or fatigued.

The Hard Breathing Technique

The name for this technique may be misleading. It is harder for beginners to do and therefore considered the more difficult of the two. When you are completely comfortable with the soft breathing technique you will easily be able to add this one. Again, the same guidelines apply. You must first be completely relaxed. Sit or lie in an appropriate position and feel all the tension draining from your body.

1. Slowly inhale through your nose and imagine that your breath is being drawn down into your lower abdomen. Concentrate on a point 3 fingers' width or approximately 2 inches below your navel. This point is known as the Dantian and is considered to be the location of a powerful concentration of Ki energy. Just relax as much as you can during this exercise and allow your mind to guide your breath downward.
2. After inhaling, pause briefly and let your tongue touch the roof of your mouth. Keep your lower abdomen expanded. Do not strain to hold your breath, just pause comfortably.
3. Let your tongue go down and exhale slowly through your nose, allowing your lower abdomen to go back in naturally during the process.

If you would like to add a deep relaxation to either of these exercises, when you breathe in think the words, "I am calm" and when you exhale think "and relaxed." You can use any other words that seem appropriate to you to feel relaxed and at peace. It is a good time to add a simple affirmation such as "I am" on the inhalation and "healthy" on the exhalation.

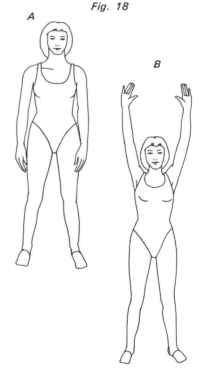

Fig. 18

A

B

Dynamic Breathing Exercise

This breathing exercise is done with large movements of the arms and legs. It has been used as an energy raising exercise for centuries.

Caution: If you have knee or back problems do not do this exercise.

1. Start in a standing position with your feet apart and your arms at your sides.
2. Raise your arms forward and upward slowly until they reach a vertical position, with fingers extended. Take a deep breath.
3. As you breathe out squat down as far as you comfortably can. Bring your arms down to your sides. You might want to hold onto something for balance the first few times you practice.

C   D

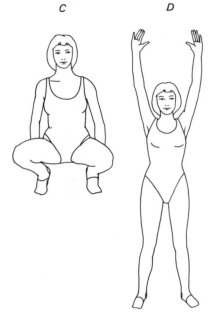

4. Repeat the standing stretch.

This exercise should be done up to ten times. If you are just starting you might do five or less and work up to ten.

The Heavenly Stretch
Whenever possible this exercise should be done outdoors. It is an excellent way to start your day and will bring balance and harmony to your mind and body.

Stand with your feet apart, bend your knees slightly and naturally. Relax both your shoulders and lift your arms with palms up.

Fig. 19

Breathe in lightly and exhale as long as you can sustain it. Try to make your breathing effortless and light.

Diaphragm Expanding Exercise
This exercise strengthens the diaphragm. It is a good technique to practice when you are feeling fatigued.

A   *Fig. 20*   B

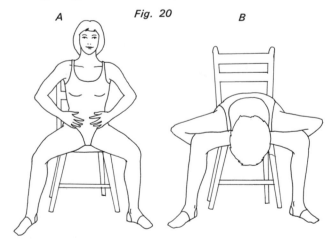

1. Sit on the edge of a chair. Stretch both feet out in front of you and place your palms on your stomach.
2. Bend the upper part of your body until your head is lower than your knees as you simultaneously press both hands against your abdomen to help move your diaphragm upward. At the same time, exhale as fully as you can.

3. Relax both hands, raise your head and stretch your neck forward while inhaling deeply as you slowly lift your body to the original position. Inhale as you stretch up. Repeat up to ten times.

Cosmic Breathing

This exercise is especially beneficial in raising your energy level. It can be combined with a series of positive thoughts which, along with the breathing and arm movements, make it beneficial for your mind and body.

Fig. 21

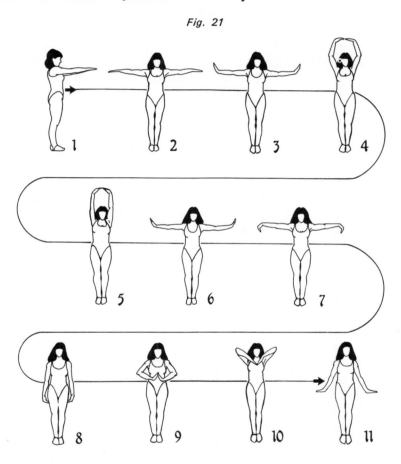

1. Stand erect with legs together and arms held relaxed at sides. Inhale and at the same time raise both arms straight out in front of you until they are parallel to the floor at shoulder height, elbows straight, fingers straight and together, palms pointing to the floor. Inhale thoughts of a sound physical body.
2. Exhale, bringing your arms sideward at right angles to the body, still at shoulder level, palms down. Exhale all ill health.
3. In one sharp motion bend the hands at the wrists until fingers point toward the ceiling. The hands are now at right angles to the arms.

4. Inhale, slowly raise your eyes toward the ceiling, and at the same time bring the hands upward in a semicircular motion until the middle fingers touch about 4 to 6 inches above the eyes, palms up. Inhale tranquility.

5. Exhale, pushing your palms toward the ceiling. Make this an extreme stretching motion, stretching both the arms and the spine. The eyes are still focused on the backs of your hands at this point. Exhale tension.

6. Inhale, slowly bring your face back to the original position and return the arms to the same position they were in after completing step *3*. Arms are parallel to the floor, fingers pointing toward the ceiling. Inhale happiness and joy.

7. In one sharp movement bend your hands at the wrists until the fingers are pointing toward the floor.

8. Exhale while bringing the straight arms downward toward the floor. Exhale fear and anger.

9. When your extended fingers are about a foot apart, begin inhaling as the arms continue toward each other. Continue inhaling, and begin pointing your fingers toward the ceiling so that you can place the hands together, back to back, fingers pointed to ceiling. Raise your hands together in this position until they are just under your chin. Inhale love and harmony.

10. Exhale as you reverse the hands so fingers point toward the floor, and bring the hands down toward the floor still back to back. The hands will part naturally at a certain point, and the arms should be brought back to the sides of the body, hands bent at the wrists, palms facing the floor. Exhale loneliness and limitation. Repeat the entire exercise three times.

• During the second round:
    Inhale positive thoughts; exhale negativity.
    Inhale an even temper; exhale irritability.
    Inhale maturity; exhale immaturity.
    Inhale generosity; exhale envy.

Yogic Breathing—Pranayama

In India, Ki is known as *prana* which is a Sanskrit word that means "vital or life-force." *Ayama* is translated as "to pause" or "to control." Therefore, in the Yogic system breathing exercises not only introduce oxygen into the lungs and blood-stream they also make it possible to gain control of the mind and body.

According to Indian sages, *pranayama* influences the flow of *prana* in the *nadis* (*pranic* or vital energy channels) which are seen to be related to the nervous system. Therefore, when you are angry or upset, the rate and force of your breath increases. Conversely, when you are relaxed or deep in thought, your breathing becomes slow and relaxed. You also breathe through your left nostril with a greater flow of air while relaxing or thinking and through your right nostril during times of excitement and physical activity. As your activities alternate the change in nostril breathing also alternates. It is felt that exhalation predominates during sleep and brings rest while inhalation predominates during the waking hours and is influenced by the external environment.

In Yoga, breathing is considered to be so important that the yogi measures life not in the number of years lived, but in the number of breaths taken during a lifetime. If a person breathes with short rapid breaths the life-force is thought to be quickly depleted. The art of breathing slowly and deeply, therefore, is thought to not only extend life but to add health and energy to every hour lived because the flow of *prana* is allowed to be free and unimpeded.

In Yoga the quality of each breath is seen to be the determining factor in how much energy you will have. Shallow respiration leaves stagnant air in the lower regions of your lungs and only by learning to breathe fully can you expect to experience vital and abundant health.

The following exercises have been chosen for their effectiveness and their simplicity. They are easy to learn and will bring many long lasting benefits.

Before Starting Pranayama
It is important to carefully consider the following guidelines:
1. The bladder and stomach should be as empty as possible.
2. The body should be relaxed. The spine, neck, and head should be centered.
3. Retention of the breath increases the amount of oxygen absorbed. It is advisable, however, to gradually build up to longer breath retention. It is important never to strain. Breath should not be retained for longer than is comfortable.
4. A well-ventilated, clean, and pleasant environment is essential to your practice.
5. Wear comfortable, loose clothing.
6. Practice when you are free from all distractions.
7. For beginners the practice of breathing exercises once or twice a day is sufficient.
8. Unless otherwise instructed, inhale through your nose.

The process of breathing can be divided into two parts: Abdominal Breathing and Thoracic or Chest Breathing.

Abdominal Breathing is also known as diaphragmatic respiration. To experience this breath sit or lie flat on your back and place one hand on your navel. Inhale deeply and the hand will rise as the abdomen expands. The diaphragm is a strong muscle membrane. The higher it moves during inhalation, the more air is inhaled into the lungs.

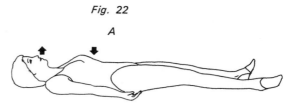

Fig. 22

A

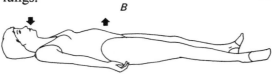

B

As you exhale deeply notice how the hand moves down as the abdomen contracts. Maximum expulsion of air from the lungs occurs if the contraction of the abdomen is accentuated.

Thoracic or Chest Breathing moves the rib cage outward and upward during inhalation. When you exhale, the ribs will move inward and downward.

During abdominal breathing it is important not to move your chest or shoulders. During thoracic breathing do not move your abdomen. By combining these types of respiration it is possible to inhale the optimum amount of air into your lungs and also exhale the maximum amount of waste air.

Cleansing *Pranayama*

The Complete Breath
This exercise increases lung capacity. It expands the chest cavity and all parts of the lungs are brought into activity. You may stand, sit or lie on your back. Your breath should be steady and continuous.

1. Fill the lower lungs by lowering the diaphragm. Your abdomen should gently expand.
2. Fill the upper portion of your lungs by expanding the lower chest.
3. Fill the upper portion of your lungs by pushing out the upper chest. Your chest will rise.
4. To fill the uppermost part of the lungs, slightly draw in the lower abdomen.
5. At the end of your inhalation, occasionally raise your shoulders to permit the air to enter the upper lobes of your lungs.
6. Retain the breath as long as you comfortably can.
7. Exhale slowly. Contract the abdomen slightly. When the air is completely exhaled, relax the chest and abdomen.
    Practice this exercise as often as possible.

Invigorating *Pranayama*
This cycle of breathing exercises will invigorate your entire system. In all of these exercises the breath is retained with the mind fully concentrating on the breath. They are done in a standing position and are designed to completely expel all the stale air in your lungs.

1. Inhale and raise arms forward, parallel with the floor.
2. Grasp an imaginary stick, hold your breath for six counts.
3. Exhale and lower your arms.

1. Inhale as completely as possible.
2. Retain the breath and tense every muscle of your body.
3. Exhale and relax.

1. Inhale and rise up onto the tips of your toes.
2. Retain the breath as long as you comfortably can.
3. Exhale and return to a normal standing position.

1. Inhale and raise both arms above your head, putting your palms together.
2. Hold your breath for six counts.
3. Exhale and lower your arms.

1. Inhale and rise up onto your toes, raise your arms above your head, palms together.
2. Hold your breath for six counts.
3. As you exhale, slowly lower your arms and relax your feet.

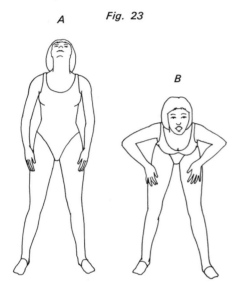

A   *Fig. 23*   *B*

The HA! Breath
This breath not only revitalizes your entire body it also is an aid in letting go of tension.

1. Tilt your head up and inhale deeply through your nose.
2. Bring your head and body forward and exhale forcefully through your mouth making a loud HA! sound that originates in your lower abdomen.
3. Repeat up to five times.

Caution: If you have a history of heart disease, high blood pressure, or stroke, go easy with this breath; transient rises in blood pressure can occur during HA!

The Lung Expander
One way to create more openness in your upper chest is to do the Lung Expander. It should be done in a standing position.
1. Place your fingertips on the top part of your shoulders.
2. Inhale through your nose as you tilt your head back and bring your elbows up, out, and back, fully expanding your chest. (Do not force this stretching motion. You may feel some tension, but there should be no pain. Stretching should never be done to the point of deep pain.)

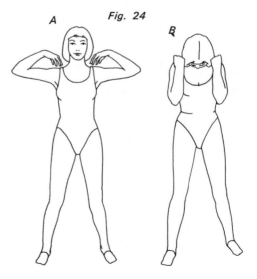

A   *Fig. 24*   *B*

3. Exhale through your mouth, bring your head down, move your elbows forward, down, and in.
4. Repeat this sequence five to ten times, feeling the opening and vitality in your chest. Start slowly, then build up a faster rhythm as the movement becomes coordinated. Remember to keep fingertips on your shoulders at all times.

Alternate Nostril Breathing

This breathing exercise is one of the most powerful and effective of all Yoga breathing exercises. It is probably one of nature's greatest tranquilizers. Use it whenever you are upset or nervous. Its calming effect is immediately felt.

The finger placement can be your choice. In the left diagram of Fig. 25, the index and middle fingers are turned down so the thumb and ring finger are close to the nose with the little finger next to the ring finger.

Fig. 25

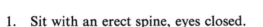

In the right diagram of Fig. 25, both fingers are placed on the space between the eyebrows, leaving the other fingers free to close the nose; with this placement, you can focus the attention on one area.

1. Sit with an erect spine, eyes closed.
2. Completely exhale from both nostrils.
3. Close the right nostril with the right thumb.
4. Draw in the air very slowly through left nostril.
5. Close the left nostril with the ring and little fingers of the right hand. (Both nostrils now closed.)
6. Pause. Remove your thumb, and exhale slowly through the right nostril.
7. Inhale slowly through the same side (right nostril).
8. Close both nostrils and pause.
9. Remove your ring and little fingers, and exhale slowly through the left nostril.
10. This constitutes one round. Start with five rounds and gradually increase the number to ten rounds.

Relaxing *Pranayama*

These breaths have a very calming influence on both mind and body.

The Waterfall

This exercise will enable you to relax deeply. The more you practice the more you will be rewarded by deep relaxation.

1. Inhale deeply.
2. Retain the breath briefly.
3. Exhale through slightly parted lips for as long as you can.
4. Repeat as often as possible.

The Cooling Breath

This exercise induces muscular relaxation, quenches thirst, and cools the body.
1. Sit with your spine erect.
2. Fold your tongue into a trough and extend it beyond your lips.
3. Inhale slowly and deeply through the folded tongue.
4. Retain the breath as long as you comfortably can.
5. Exhale through the nose.

The Droning Breath

When the breath is slowly released with a controlled humming, resonance is felt in the upper nasal passages between your eyebrows. This will produce a deep relaxation.
1. Inhale deeply.
2. With the lips slightly parted, hum as you exhale.
3. Repeat three times without stopping.

Exercise

The Western Concept

In the Western societies there is a growing concern about health, weight, appearance, and a desire for increased longevity. Billions of dollars are now being spent annually in an effort to get into better physical condition. More and more of the top ten best sellers in hardcover nonfiction are books having to do with diet or fitness. Workout video tapes have become increasingly popular as have health and exercise clubs. There is also a trend to convert living space into private gyms with millions of dollars spent on various fitness devices. It is estimated that the amount of money spent on fitness yearly is nearly as much as is spent for camping, golf, and racquet sports combined.

According to a nationwide U.S. Department of Health and Human Services survey released in May, 1986, it was shown that 80 percent of Americans still do not get enough consistent exercise. The Public Health Service defines consistent exercise as anything that boosts heart and lung performance to 60 percent or more of its capacity at least three times a week for a full twenty minutes, the minimum needed to produce any cardiovascular benefit. In 1980 the Health Service urged that by 1990, three-fifths of those eighteen to sixty-four and half of those sixty-five and over should be meeting that minimum.

Although it is not possible to predict whether this goal will be met, there is mounting evidence that most people are at least aware of the need for participating in some form of physical activity and increasing numbers of people are becoming motivated to exercise on a regular basis.

One of the major forces behind the new exercise consciousness is the evidence that civilized people are dying of heart and blood vessel disease at epidemic rates because of their sedentary ways. It has been proven by many leading medical schools that exercise keeps arteries open, helps control weight and vigorous exercise keeps arteries open, helps control weight and reduces blood pressure and pulse rates; all of which benefit the heart. It is a fundamental physiological fact that most systems of the body become more efficient with greater use. This is especially true of muscles, and the heart is a muscle.

More than one half of your body is comprised of muscle and every muscle is there to be used. Muscles work together in pairs and in groups. When one group of muscles contracts, the opposite group relaxes. No single muscle works alone. If groups of muscles are not used, or used too little, they tend to deteriorate and lose their strength, firmness, and elasticity (they lose their tone). Muscles which are not used enough become weak and flabby. If there is extra fat in your body, it will gravitate to, and settle around, muscles which are not in tone. Weak and flabby muscles cannot break up fat and move it out of your system. When fat settles around muscles, they stretch and sag and, in turn, cause the surrounding tissues to sag as well. Extra fat may make your body look firm, but a weight loss will not make the muscles firm and strong, only exercise can produce strength and firmness.

Those who exercise consistently know that to be vibrantly alive is to be in motion. When you are active your energy level increases and you radiate health and vitality. Exercise is what makes your body thrive because the body was created for activity.

Our bodies have not changed from a time in the not too distant past when running, walking, and lifting for many hours was the rule rather than the exception. With the advent of more and more machines to do the work, strenuous living and working conditions have virtually been eliminated for most of the population.

By following both the Western and Eastern concepts of exercise you can gain the knowledge and the motivation that you need to become active with a trim, beautiful body that radiates health and vitality.

Your Complete Exercise Program

There are three basic components to an exercise program.
1. Aerobic exercise (heart and lung fitness).
2. Flexibility exercises. The bending and stretching of these exercises increases your range of motion and keeps your spine and joints flexible along with corresponding muscle groups.
3. Muscle strength and endurance; which consists of thickening muscle fiber mass to enable you to endure a heavier work load for a longer period of time without fatigue.

Aerobic Exercise

Most simply stated, the term "aerobic" means promoting the supply and use of oxygen. By stressing continuous movement at a self-monitored level, aerobic exercise requires your body to demand increased amounts of oxygen over an extended period of time. The resulting aerobic fitness leads to an increase in health and energy.

Benefits of Aerobic Exercise
1. You are able to continue vigorous activities for a reasonably long period of time without becoming breathless or overly fatigued.
2. Your body systems recover quickly from an active workout, or any other strenuous activity.
3. Your hunger is regulated. Aerobic exercise tends to decrease hunger physiologically by requiring blood to be "borrowed" from less active body systems, such as the stomach, and delivered to the more active skeletal muscle system. Until the blood supply is returned to your stomach, you will not have as much of a desire for food.
4. You have more daily energy as your body systems become more efficient.
5. You will burn calories efficiently. Aerobic workouts or sports are high calorie-burners because they demand energy. You can expect to burn about 250 to 300 calories in a moderate forty-five minute aerobic exercise class,

which is equivalent to bicycling for forty-five minutes at seven miles per hour. (If you weigh 117 pounds and watch television for forty-five minutes, you burn approximately 75 calories.)

6. Improved circulation allows your muscles, skin, and vital organs to receive a better supply of blood, which contributes to a healthier body tone.

7. When you exercise vigorously, you continue to burn more calories following exercise than you would during normal activity. For as long as six hours after a forty-five minute session of aerobic activity you can expect to burn about twice as many calories while resting as you would if you had remained inactive.

8. You will be vigorously exercising the most important muscle of your body—your heart. This produces the training effect which is the major goal of an aerobic exercise program.

Enjoying Aerobic Exercise

There are four steps to consider taking if you are just starting a program of regular aerobic activity.

Step 1

If you have not exercised regularly, have recently had surgery, are thirty-five or more years of age, are significantly overweight, or have specific physical limitations, you should have a physician's approval before you start to exercise.

A thorough medical examination is the recommended way to make sure that your current state of health and your physical capacity are adequate to safely engage in vigorous physical activity.

Step 2

Choose wearing apparel that will promote comfort and ease of movement. Select cotton material for doing vigorous exercise because it absorbs perspiration better than other fabrics. Dress in layers so that as you exercise you can stay comfortable by removing top layers of clothing.

Your choice of shoes is important. Well-constructed shoes are a must for aerobic exercise. They should not only insure your comfort but will help to prevent injuries, particularly if this type of exercise is new to you.

Select a shoe that is designed to take the stress of repeated shock to your knees, lower legs, ankles, and feet. Your shoe should have support in the arch and heel and the sole should be thick enough to cushion the effects of heavy bouncing movements.

Step 3

Warm up before you start and cool down when you have finished. These two phases are extremely important, and often overlooked. There are two goals for the warm-up: The first is to stretch and warm up the muscles of your back and extremities. The second is to encourage a slight acceleration of your heart rate so that you can move more gradually into the higher heart rate of the aerobic phase.

The cool down is equally important and should take a minimum of five minutes. As you cool down you are moving at a slower pace which will allow your heart rate to decline gradually. Your blood pools in your legs during strenuous aerobic exercise and must be pumped back into the central circulatory system. If you omit this step you could become dizzy or light-headed.

Step 4
Determine your target heart rate. To get the most benefit from your exercise it is necessary to maintain a sufficiently high heart rate. This will enable you to establish certain beneficial cardiovascular changes called the "training effect."

It is important to understand how to monitor your heart rate. This will enable you to pace yourself during your workout. The technique for monitoring your heart rate is given on page 102.

Choosing an Aerobic Activity
Among the popular activities that provide the best aerobic conditioning potential, the top seven, listed in descending order of exercise value, are:

1. Cross-country Skiing
This sport involves more muscles than any other activity. When a maximum number of muscles are used simultaneously you achieve a more aerobic benefit. Altitude and cold weather also play a part in providing a rigorous workout.

2. Swimming
Swimming also involves all of the major muscles in the body. It is also possible to swim long distances without pressure on your joints and bones.

3. Jogging or Running
This is the most convenient exercise. It is highly recommended that you run on a natural surface rather than on pavement which may be injurious to your joints.

4. Outdoor Cycling
For the best result you should cycle at a rate slightly greater than fifteen miles per hour. This exercise causes less strain on joints and muscles than running. If you have joint problems you might wish to consider cycling as an excellent alternative to running.

5. Fast Walking
For walking to produce an aerobic benefit it must be brisk and of sufficient length to maintain your target heart rate. It takes about three times as long to get the same aerobic benefit from walking as from running but it does not strain joints, bones, and muscles.

6. Roller Skating and Skating
Skating at a speed of ten miles per hour is the aerobic equivalent of jogging at five

miles per hour. You must skate continuously, without coasting, to maintain your target heart rate.

7. Aerobic Dancing

The best way to choose a class that will give you the benefit of consistent aerobic activity is to try a few different ones before you decide to enroll on a regular basis. To be certain that your activity is providing you the benefit you expect, you should monitor your heart rate to be sure you are expending enough energy during your workout.

Monitoring Your Heart Rate

Your pulse rate tells you the number of heartbeats per minute and can best be counted at two pulsation points. You should select the area at which you can easily obtain a pulse with your index and second fingers. The first point is on the side of your neck and the second is on the thumb side of your wrist.

Fig. 26   Fig. 27

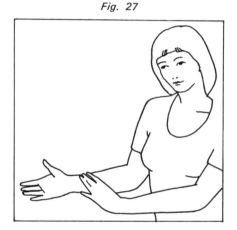

The carotid artery runs up the side of your neck and is easy to find. Place your index and middle fingers at the point of your jaw bone and slide downward an inch or so, pressing lightly.

The radial artery runs up the inside of your wrist on the thumb side. Place your index and middle fingers on the artery at the wrist. Press lightly.

Count the number of pulsations or beats for each six seconds and multiply by 10 (add a zero). The total is the number of heartbeats per minute.

Your heart rate will increase after vigorous activity and should return to normal within a short period of time after resting. As a rule, the faster it slows down (recovers from exercise), the more physically fit you are.

When you take your pulse rate during aerobic exercise and find that your pace is below your established training zone, you need to increase the intensity of your workout. If you are recording a pulse rate that is higher you need to lower your intensity.

Heartbeats per Minute

Age	Maximum Heart Rate	Exercise Heart Range
20	200	140–170
21	199	139–169
22	198	139–168
23	197	138–168
24	196	137–167
25	195	137–166
26	194	136–165
27	193	135–164
28	192	134–164
29	191	134–163
30	190	133–162
31	189	132–161
32	188	132–160
33	187	131–159
34	186	130–158
35	185	130–157
36	184	129–156
37	183	128–156
38	182	127–155
39	181	127–154
40	180	126–153
41	179	125–152
42	178	125–151
43	177	125–151
44	176	123–149
45	175	122–149
46	174	122–148
47	173	121–147
48	172	120–146
49	171	120–145
50	170	119–145
51	169	118–144
52	168	118–143
53	167	117–142
54	166	116–141
55	165	116–140
56	164	115–139
57	163	114–139
58	162	113–138
59	161	113–137
60	160	112–136
61	159	111–135
62	158	111–134
63	157	110–134
64	156	109–133
65 and above	155	109–132

What Your Heart Rate Tells You

One of the goals of an aerobic exercise program is to lower the resting heart rate, helping the heart to become a stronger pump, to work less, and to function more efficiently.

Everyone has three important heart rates: the resting heart rate, the working heart rate, and the recovery heart rate. All three indicate something about your level of fitness.

The average *Resting Heart Rate* for women is 78 to 84 beats a minute; for men it falls between 72 to 78 beats per minute. A person in good aerobic condition usually has a lower resting heart rate than a person in poor aerobic condition. After a program in aerobic conditioning, many people find that their resting heart rate decreases significantly, indicating that their hearts have become stronger.

The *Working Heart Rate* tells how hard you are working and indicates whether you are exercising at a safe but effective level. As the aerobic exercises become more vigorous and more oxygen is required, the heart increases its rate of beating to supply oxygen to the muscles.

The *Recovery Heart Rate* is taken after exercise stops. Like the working heart rate, the recovery rate tells you if you are working at a safe level. Five minutes after you have stopped exercising, the heart rate should not exceed 120. After ten minutes, the count should be below 100. If not, you have overextended yourself and should exercise less rigorously.

How to Compute Your Working Heart Rate Range

This example is for a person who is forty years of age with a resting heart rate of 72 who has chosen to exercise at the 50 percent capacity. There is also space for you to calculate your working heart rate range.

	Example	*For you*
220 minus your age	180	_____
Subtract your resting heart rate (best done first thing in the morning or after 15 minutes of rest)	−72	−
Answer:	108	_____
Multiply by 0.5 or 0.6 or 0.7 or 0.8 (Capacity of 50%, 60%, 70%, 80% exercise)	×0.5	×
Answer	54	_____
Add your Resting Heart Rate:	+72	+
Your Working Heart Rate per minute	126	_____
Divide by 10 to find beats per 6 seconds:	12	_____

Basic Principles of Stretching

Stretching should be performed in a static position meaning once you obtain a comfortable stretch you should *hold it;* do not bounce. Bouncing can cause small tears in the muscles and will also cause the muscle to reflexively contract, actually tightening the muscle instead of relaxing it.

The position of stretch should be comfortable, it should not *hurt*. You should be able to hold a stretch for a long period without discomfort.

Stretching should be done before exercise as a warm-up for muscles, joints, and ligaments. Also you can stretch anytime you want to relax, especially after exercise.

• *Keys to stretching:*
Move your body into the desired position and hold an easy stretch in which you barely feel any tension for 20 to 30 seconds.

In between stretches you can relax and "shake out" your muscles for a few seconds.

Next maintain a position in which you feel a considerable tension and stretch the muscle for at least 30 seconds (longer if you feel particularly tight in that area). This part of the stretch is called the developmental stretch and is where the most gain in flexibility is obtained. Then relax and repeat.

Remember to consciously focus on the part of the muscle that is tight and try to relax that part.

Always breathe deeply and regularly while stretching; never hold your breath.

Stretches from Head to Toes
This basic series of stretches can serve as a framework for a stretching program to which you can add new stretches as needed. It includes stretches for all of the major muscle groups and proceeds in an easily remembered sequence starting with your head and ending with your lower extremities.

Front Thigh Stretch (or Quadriceps Stretch)
First find a wall or sturdy object on which you can lean one arm to support yourself. Next, bend the leg to be stretched at the knee and hold onto your lower leg at the ankle with your nonsupporting hand. Gently and slowly begin to stretch the thigh muscles by extending the thigh backward. Hold the stretch for 20 to 30 seconds. Relax and repeat two times on each leg.

Fig. 28

Groin Stretch
In the sitting position, bend both legs so that the soles of your feet are flat against each other and your knees fall toward the ground. Hold your feet

Fig. 29

with your hands and attempt to pull your chest toward your feet. Again, hold an easy stretch for 20 to 30 seconds, relax then hold a developmental stretch for another 20 to 30 seconds. This exercise stretches the muscles in the groin area.

Fig. 30

Calf Stretch (or "Wall Push")

Stand facing a wall or other sturdy structure (such as a tree) and place your hands on the wall so that they are able to support your body weight. Place one foot in front of the other about 18 inches apart. Make sure that both feet are parallel and that the heel of your back leg is kept on the ground. Keeping your back straight, let your body lean toward the wall. You may need to bend the knee of your front leg slightly to get a better stretch. Remember to keep your back leg straight. Do this for both legs by changing foot positions.

This stretch should be done every day, especially before exercising. Women who usually wear high heels should do this stretch more often because heels tend to cause the calf muscles to shorten and become tight.

A

Fig. 31

B

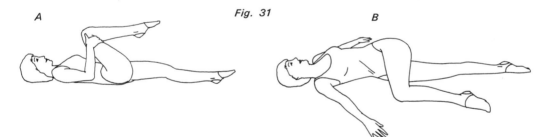

Leg and Back Stretches

Lie on your back, bend one leg and hold your thigh behind your knee with both hands. Pull your knee to your chest until you feel a comfortable stretch in the back of your thigh and in the lower back. Hold an easy stretch for 20 to 30 seconds, relax and then hold a developmental stretch for another 20 to 30 seconds. Next, allow the leg that you just stretched to gently cross over your extended leg and try to put your knee to the ground. Keep your shoulders flat on the ground.

Extend your arms out to help you balance. You should feel a very comfortable stretch in your lower back area and in your side muscles. Do this complete stretch for both legs. It is an excellent way to relax and relieve tensions and fatigue in your lower back.

Your calf and hamstring muscles should always be stretched immediately before walking or jogging to prevent soreness and injury.

Breathing: Always exhale on the effort.

Benefits of Specific Activities

Activity	Upper	Middle	Lower	Cardio-respiratory	Flexibility
Basketball	fair	fair	good	good	good
Bicycling	fair	poor	good	great	fair
Canoeing	good	good	poor	fair-to-good	poor
Dirt biking	good	good	good	good	fair
Golf	fair	fair	good	poor	fair
Horseback riding	fair	fair	fair	fair	fair
Karate	good	good	good	fair	great
Racquetball	good	fair	good	good	fair
Running	good	fair	good	good	fair
Scuba diving	fair	fair	fair	poor	fair
Skating (ice/roller)	poor	poor	good	fair-to-good	fair
Skiing (cross-country)	great	good	great	good-to-great	good
Skiing (downhill)	good	good	good	fair	good
Soccer	fair	great	good	good	good
Softball	fair	fair	good	poor-to-fair	fair
Surfing	good	fair	fair	good	fair
Swimming	good	good	fair	great	good
Tennis	good	good	fair	fair-to-good	fair
Volleyball	fair	fair	fair	fair	fair
Walking (brisk)	good	good	good	good	fair
Water-skiing	good	fair	good	poor	fair
Weight training	great	great	great	fair	good

Muscle Strength and Endurance

Muscular strength and endurance are closely related. However, it is important to differentiate between the two. Strength is defined as the amount of force (weight) a muscle or group of muscles can exert for one repetition. It is generally measured by a single maximal contraction, endurance is the capacity of the same muscle or group of muscles to sustain a series of repetitive contractions.

Muscle strength is defined as the ability to exert a force against a resistance. The force is, specifically, the tightening, and stretching of your two opposing muscle groups around the same joint against the resistance provided by a free weight, a weight machine, or the weight of your own body against gravity. This kind of strength provides you with the ability to establish correct body alignment and to support your internal organs. It enables you to control your body movements with agility, coordination, and poise. It also is the component most needed for performing difficult sport skills.

Muscle endurance allows you to repeat the contraction and extension of a particular muscle group numerous times without undue fatigue. For example, it takes muscle endurance to sustain heavy work or practice any of the aerobic activities for a reasonable length of time.

Muscle strength and endurance go together because by improving your strength you are able to meet your daily physical demands with ease. You tire less readily and have the necessary body control to move with confidence through a great range of motion. With greater endurance you can continue your activities as long as you wish without having to stop to gather the energy to continue.

Benefits of Muscle Strength and Endurance

You look and feel better. Your energy is directed outward to the tasks you wish to accomplish rather than inward, which is the case when you experience excessive tiredness and muscle fatigue.

Your muscles are more defined and toned and your posture makes you appear self-confident.

You have the ability to sustain a continual aerobic activity which provides you with all of the benefits this type of activity produces.

You slow the aging process by making sure your muscles are toned and well-developed.

Muscle Function

The function of skeletal muscle is to produce tension (force) which is generally translated into movement. Muscles are attached to bones by connective tissue called tendons. A skeletal muscle is attached between two bones. Contraction of the muscle produces force, which can move one bone through a range of degrees toward the other bone. The bone that remains stationary is considered the origin of the muscle and the bone that moves is referred to as the insertion.

Fig. 32

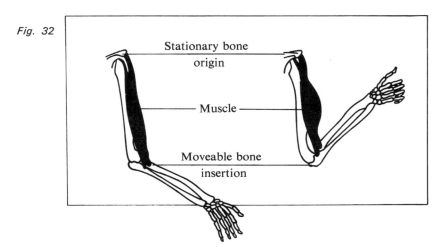

Stationary bone
origin

Muscle

Moveable bone
insertion

Strength and endurance exercises are designed to utilize and increase the muscular force around specific joint movements. Following is a visual explanation of the movement of the major joints and muscle groups.

Fig. 33

Fig. 34

Muscle flexion

• *A Word of Caution*

If you are planning to try a weight training program, the only way to be certain that you are doing the exercises correctly and without injury is to find qualified instruction.

There are many such programs available at fitness centers, the YMCA and most colleges and universities.

Strength and Endurance Exercises

An exercise program for strength and endurance will tone your entire body and increase your energy in many ways. These exercises are based on the overload principle which means that your muscles will become stronger in response to the demand you place on them. Some obvious benefits of keeping your muscles in good condition are that you will be able to carry heavy objects with less strain and be less tired after engaging in strenuous activities. There are also other benefits which are extremely important. For example, strong muscles work in support of your heart. When your muscles relax, they fill with blood. When they contract, that blood is pumped toward your heart. Also, with regular exercise the size of the muscle fibers increases thereby enabling you to have a reserve supply of strength and energy.

Strength and endurance can be built by increasing the number of repetitions for each exercise over a period of several weeks. For best results start with the number of repetitions that you can do without tiring. Increase gradually until you can do approximately twenty-five repetitions in each category. If you are unable to exercise for a week or more, start your program at a lower level and slowly work back to where you left off.

When you feel comfortable with one level of difficulty go on to the next. Regular breathing is essential when doing the following exercises. (Always exhale on the effort.) It is also important to start with at least five minutes of stretching before you begin.

Stomach Muscles

Beginner

Lie on your back, palms on the floor, legs straight, and feet close together.

Fig. 35

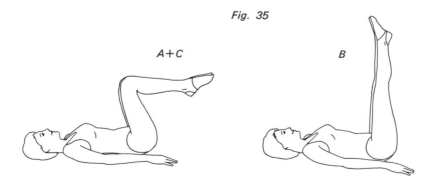

A+C   B

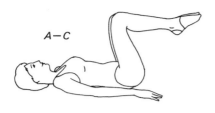

A – C

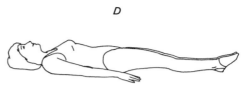

D

1. Bring your knees to your chest, heels as close to your buttocks as possible. Keep your legs together.
2. Stretch your legs up until they are at right angles to the floor. Your feet should be together and your toes pointed.
3. Return to position *1*.
4. Return to your starting position.

Fig. 36

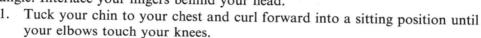

A

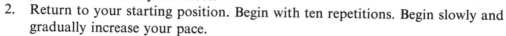

B

Intermediate

Lie on your back with your knees bent at an angle. Interlace your fingers behind your head.

1. Tuck your chin to your chest and curl forward into a sitting position until your elbows touch your knees.
2. Return to your starting position. Begin with ten repetitions. Begin slowly and gradually increase your pace.

Fig. 37

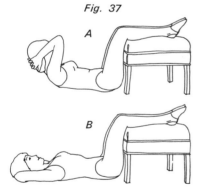

A

B

Advanced

Lie on your back with your knees bent and your calves resting on a chair or bench. Interlace your fingers behind your head.

1. Tuck your chin to your chest and curl forward to a sitting position. Hold for three seconds.
2. Return to your starting position. Begin with ten repetitions.

Upper Body

Beginner

Stand as straight as you can. Place your feet shoulder width apart.

1. Raise one arm over your head and bend to the side. Keep your stomach tucked firm. Continue to stretch to the side until you feel that you cannot go further. Hold the position for six counts.

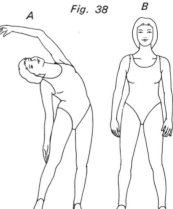

A   *Fig. 38*   B

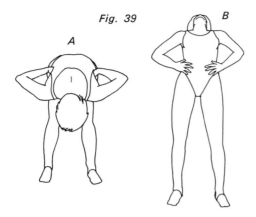

Fig. 39

2. Return to the starting position and repeat to the other side.

Intermediate and Advanced
Do the above exercise and add a bend forward from the waist and a backward bend from the waist. Hold each position for a count of six.

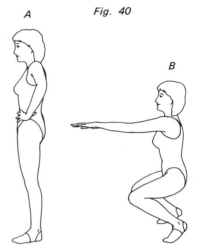

Fig. 40

Legs, Hips, Buttocks, and Lower Back

Beginner
Stand with your feet comfortably apart. Place your hands on your hips.
1. Bend your knees to a half squat position as you swing your arms forward with palms down. (*Caution:* do not exceed the half squat position.)
2. Return to the starting position.

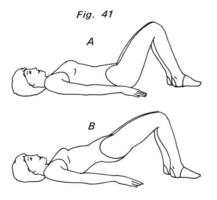

Fig. 41

Intermediate
Lie on your back with your knees bent and your feet about shoulder width apart. Rest your arms at your sides with palms down.
1. Raise your hips off the floor keeping your feet and shoulders on the floor. Tighten your buttocks and stomach muscles and hold for six seconds.
2. Slowly return to your starting position.

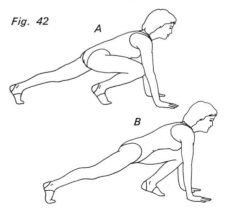

Fig. 42

Advanced
With your hands touching the floor directly under your shoulders, extend your left leg back and place your right knee inside your right elbow.
1. Remain in the position for six counts and then reverse the position of your legs.
2. Each time you reverse, change slowly and carefully.

Arms, Shoulders, and Chest

Beginner

Stand with your feet apart, head held high and your back as straight as possible. Extend your arms to the side, shoulder height.

1. Starting with your palms up, quickly open and close your hands. When they close turn your palms down.
2. Add arm circles in both directions.
3. Move at a pace that is comfortable for you.

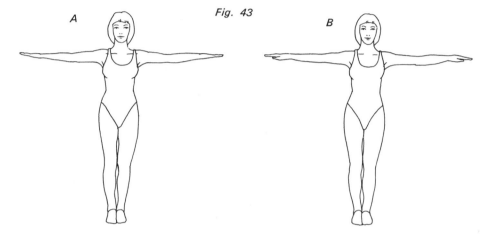

Fig. 43

A

B

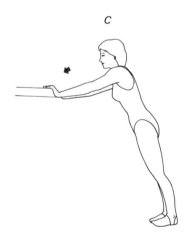

C

Place your hands shoulder width apart on the edge of a solid object. Move your feet back until your legs and back are in a straight line. Be sure you are completely supported by your hands and feet.

1. Bend your arms at the elbow and lower your body until your chest touches the object.
2. Push away by straightening your arms. Return to the starting position. Move at a moderate pace.

Intermediate

Place your hands on the floor with arms directly underneath your shoulders. Head up and back straight. Rest your weight on your hands and knees.

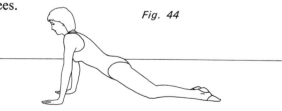

Fig. 44

1. Slowly lower and raise your body. Exhale as you push up and inhale as you come down.

Advanced

Place your hands on the floor with arms directly underneath your shoulders. Keep your head up and your back straight. Rest your weight on your hands and toes.

1.   Keep your legs straight and slowly lower and raise your body.
2.   Lower your chest to the floor. Repeat moving at a moderate pace.

Fig. 45

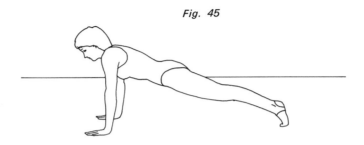

The Eastern Concept

In the Orient it has long been a tradition to start each day with graceful flowing movements. During the early morning hours it is a common sight to see groups of people participating in some form of exercise. At present, especially in the larger cities of Japan, aerobic exercise has also found thousands of devotees. For example, one of the favorite routes of Tokyo joggers is around the ancient Imperial Palace.

Whether jogging or practicing Tai Chi, there is a general consensus in all of the Eastern societies that certain kinds of exercises are helpful in promoting energy and vitality. In contrast to many Western exercise programs that emphasize strength and competition, the Eastern way is to strive for balance and harmony of mind, body, and spirit. For those who exercise regularly in this tradition, the following concepts are of importance:

Vibratory Energy
Since all physiological processes are accompanied by some degree of electrical activity, it is important to discover and practice exercise methods which can supply your body with an abundant quantity of Ki.

For hundreds of years, the Eastern cultures have been successful in raising Ki energy levels through the use of body movements that employ a high degree of balance and control. Eastern health practitioners believe that these exercises stimulate the energetic charge in your muscles, which is the same as that of an electric current passing along a wire. Therefore, the quality of the vibrations in your body and the regularity of their occurrence can become a factor in raising or lowering your energy levels.

Centering and Grounding
Another important concept in the Eastern exercise systems is that of being centered and grounded. This denotes a feeling of stability from the top of your head to your feet and into the ground. The immediate result of this experience is that you feel secure. The Japanese saying, *Hara ni chikara o ireru* means "to concentrate one's whole strength in the abdomen (*Hara*) for stability." When you are balanced and centered in the Dantian, you are better able to experience a state of calm and ease. All of your movements then become effortless and flowing.

To be grounded is another way to express the idea that you know where you stand, and therefore, you know fully who you are. Being grounded you have "sure footing" in a broader sense, which represents your contact with the basic realities of your life.

Karlfried Durckheim wrote in *Hara: The Vital Center of Man*,

When a man possesses a fully developed Hara he has the strength and precision to perform actions which otherwise he could never achieve even with the most perfected technique, the closest attention or the strongest willpower. Only what is done with Hara succeeds completely.

Mental Discipline

The Eastern traditions teach that although it is important to practice a skill it is even more important to master thoughts that are connected with that skill's performance. For example, the discipline of *Kendo*, or the art of handling a sword, is seen as both a physical and mental discipline of the highest order. This ancient art is still popular in Japan today.

Many universities, the police, and the military all have flourishing Kendo clubs which hold nationwide contests. Instead of real swords, the Kendo enthusiasts practice with stout shafts made of split bamboo bound together in the form of a sword. In this sport, as in all of the other martial arts, one learns to become grounded and centered as well as focused. This mental discipline, taught from an early age, enables those who practice these arts to achieve a high degree of composure during many stressful situations.

Gracefulness

Typically, the Oriental approach to all movement is with controlled grace. Dancing has been a part of the Eastern cultures for centuries. Their style of dance combines graceful movements with intricate steps and often with the use of elaborate and colorful costumes. These movements have been carried over to many of the exercises that are regularly performed.

Experiencing Ki through Exercise

The following exercises have been chosen for their ability to promote a high level of Ki energy and to enhance your vitality, balance, and poise. Many of them do not require a lengthy warm-up, however we suggest that you start with a few simple stretches before you begin the more strenuous exercises. All of the exercises include movements which are flowing and natural. Therefore, you will experience a feeling of lightness and energy during your practice because you will be releasing tension and stiffness in your body. As you continue each day, you will find that your range of motion is gradually increasing, which will enable you to move even more easily and comfortably.

It will be of benefit if you can find a natural setting for your practice. However, if conditions and weather do not permit, you may wish to use an exercise mat made of natural materials.

Your clothing should be loose and comfortable and your practice room well ventilated. For the most benefit you should practice the exercises of your choice for at least twenty minutes, three times a week.

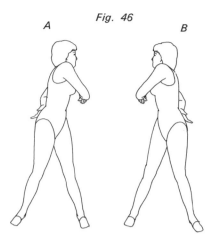

Fig. 46

A   B

Warm-up Exercises

Trunk Rotation
1. Stand erect and bend your knees slightly.
2. Gently allow your arms to swing freely.
3. Twist from side to side in a moderate and relaxed manner while allowing your closed fists to gently hit your sides and back.
4. Breathe deeply as you twist.
5. Repeat ten times.

Wake-up Exercise
1. Stand or kneel and make a fist with both hands.
2. Lightly tap or slap your chest and rib cage twenty times.
3. Bend forward and lightly tap or slap your lower back.
4. From a standing position, bend forward and briskly slap the back of your knees twenty times.

Caution: Do not talk while you are doing these exercises or use excessive force.

Whole Body Stretch

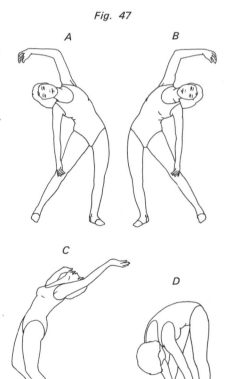

Fig. 47

A   B

C

D

1. From a standing position with your feet shoulder width apart, bend to the right side. Bend your knees slightly to relax your back. Hold the stretch for a slow count of four. Inhale and change to the other side. Stretch from side to side four times. Breathe deeply.
2. From the same standing position stretch back as far as you can with your knees bent. Your arms should be over your head, stretching back. Remain in this posture as long as you comfortably can. When you are ready to release the backward posture bring your arms forward, inhale and come to the original position.
3. Bend as far forward as you comfortably can. Relax your head, your arms and slightly bend your knees. Stay in the posture as long as you wish and then repeat the sequence.
4. Repeat four times when you are beginning this exercise (for the first few times). As you become more flexible you will wish to remain in the posture longer and add more repetitions.

Five Animal Play

In China many people enjoy the benefits of the following exercises. They are called *Wu Chin Hsi*, "Five Animal Play" and were developed by Hua To, a Chinese physician, several thousand years ago. Many versions of Five Animal Play exist at the present time. The version we have selected is one that is often performed.

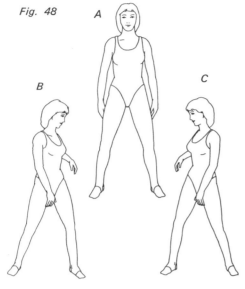

Fig. 48

Bear Play

1. Stand with your feet apart and your arms at your sides. Take several deep breaths.
2. Move your lower body in your version of a bear-like movement.
3. Bend your right knee slightly and swing your right shoulder downward to the front with your arm hanging naturally. Rotate your left shoulder slightly backward and lift your left hand.
4. Reverse the movement to the other side. Breathe deeply and regularly.
5. Repeat as often as you wish.

   Bear play is thought to improve digestion, joint mobility, and respiration.

When you practice center your attention in the Hara or Dantian (in China it is called the *Tan-Tien*).

Move slowly and gracefully.

Tiger Play

1. Stand naturally with your arms at your sides.
2. Place your heels together and turn out your toes.
3. Touch your tongue to the roof of your mouth.

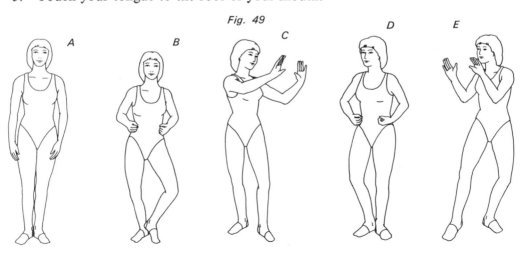

Fig. 49

4. As you make a fist with both hands pull your lower arms in so that your hands, palms up, fingers facing you, come to the center of your waist.
5. Look toward the left.
6. Simultaneously, bend your knees and place your weight on your right leg. Bring the heel of your left foot close to your right ankle.
7. Lift your fists toward your chest with the fingers facing your body. At mouth and chin level turn your fists, open your hands, and push out strongly at chest level with your palms.
8. The "tigers' mouth" is the space between your thumbs and index fingers.
9. Look at the tip of your left index finger.
10. Repeat this exercise to the other side focusing your eyes on your fingers to the right.
11. Repeat as often as you wish.

The exercise should be done with the quickness and grace of a tiger. Be composed yet fierce. Keep your focus in the Hara.

This is an excellent exercise for balance and for arm and leg strength.

Monkey Play
1. Stand naturally with your arms at your sides.
2. Raise your left hand up beside your chest. As soon as it reaches the level of your mouth and chin, make it into a claw and thrust it forward as if you were reaching out to grasp something.
3. Simultaneously, bend your knees slowly.
4. Step forward with your left foot.

Fig. 50

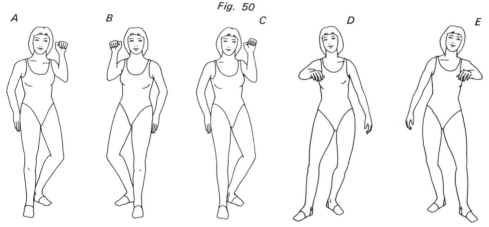

A   B   C   D   E

5. Raise your right hand up to your chest. When your hand is opposite your mouth and chin, thrust it forward in a claw-like position with your wrist bent. Bring your left hand back to your side with the elbow slightly bent.
6. Simultaneously step forward with your right foot and lift your left heel slightly.
7. Raise your left hand. When it is level with your mouth, thrust it forward in a claw and draw your right hand back to your side.

8. Simultaneously, move your left foot behind you and place it on the ground. Bend your left knee and shift your weight onto your left leg.
9. Move your right foot back slightly and lift your heel while keeping your toes on the ground.
10. Bring your right hand up in front of your chest. Make a claw and extend it in a grasping motion as soon as it is level with your mouth and chin.
11. Simultaneously take one quick step forward with your right foot.
12. Bring your left hand up to your chest. When it is at mouth and chin level, thrust it forward in a claw. Bring your right hand back to your side with the elbow bent.
13. Step forward with your left foot and again with the right foot.
14. Lift your right heel while keeping your toes on the ground.
15. Bring your right hand up to your chest. When it reaches mouth and chin level, thrust it forward in a claw. Draw your left hand back to your side with the elbow bent to complete the exercise.
16. Simultaneously, step back with your right foot and place it firmly on the ground. Bend your knee and shift your weight.
17. Move your left leg slightly backward also. Lift your heel and keep your toes down. This completes one set of the exercise.

This exercise should be done gracefully and with complete balance. When you are beginning to learn the exercise you might practice the arm movements and leg movements separately until it feels natural to do them together. Keep your mental focus in the Dantian and your eyes on your dominant hand.

This is an excellent exercise for poise and for concentration.

Fig. 51

Deer Play

1. Begin in a standing position and reach forward with your left hand, palm open and turned inward. The arm should be shoulder height and the elbow slightly bent.
2. Reach forward with your right hand, with the palm and fingers also turned inward.
3. Bring your right hand parallel to your left elbow.
4. Simultaneously, bend your right knee, and draw your upper body back.
5. Extend your left leg forward with your knee slightly bent, keeping your weight on your right leg.
6. Moving from your waist, rotate your arms in a counter-clockwise circle in front of your body. (Repeat the circle several times.)
7. Feel the flexibility in your spine as you circle your arms.
8. Repeat the exercise to the other side, rotating your arms in a clockwise circle.

The exercise is based on the notion that the deer frequently shakes its tail. When you rotate your arms, your coccyx (the deer's tail) will rotate in a smaller circle.

This exercise increases the movement and flexibility of your lower body. It also stimulates the kidneys and improves the circulation in your legs and pelvic cavity.

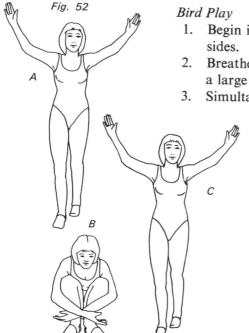

Fig. 52

Bird Play

1. Begin in a standing position with your arms at your sides.
2. Breathe in deeply and raise your arms upward in a large "V."
3. Simultaneously step forward with your left foot.
4. Take a half step with your right foot keeping your toes in contact with the floor.
5. Take another step with your right foot to bring it parallel with your left foot.
6. Squat down as far as you comfortably can, hold onto your knees and exhale fully.
7. Come back to a standing position.
8. Stretch your arms upward again and inhale.
9. Simultaneously, take a step forward with your right foot.
10. Follow with two half steps with your left foot.
11. Repeat the rest of the sequence alternating the foot pattern as many times as you wish.

This is an excellent exercise for your heart, lungs, kidneys, lower body, and legs. As you stretch up, feel lightness and a sense of flight.

Hand Swinging

Li Shou or hand swinging is a simple and very effective way to raise your energy. It is an exercise you can practice anywhere and at any time.

Fig. 53

1. Stand in a comfortable position with your feet shoulder width apart. Your arms should be totally relaxed and your hands loose and comfortable.
2. Look straight ahead and focus your attention at the Dantian.
3. When you are ready gently begin swinging your arms and hands. Your thumbs should not be allowed to swing higher than your navel and your little fingers should not go higher than your buttocks.
4. Keep your knees bent and your entire body relaxed.
5. Breathe naturally and regularly. Do not attempt to coordinate your breathing with the swinging or count the number of swings as either of these would tend to distract you.

6. Swing for as long as you wish taking care not to overdo it. You will be able to work up to longer and longer periods of swinging gradually.

Practice Li Shou often when you are feeling fatigued. You will soon find that you can increase your energy each time you practice.

The Arch or Bow

This is an ancient exercise that is used to center and ground the body. It is thought that when a body is in this position it is perfectly balanced. Dynamically, when a bow is drawn it is ready for action. In this position the body is energetically

Fig. 54

charged from head to toe, therefore, you will feel vibrations in your legs and torso.

The position is used to give a sense of being connected or integrated with the earth and also with the sky because you are looking up as you stretch.

1. Stand with your feet comfortably apart.
2. Place your hands flat on your lower back.
3. Stretch as far back as you comfortably can.
4. Take deep, relaxing breaths as you stretch.
5. Hold the stretch as long as you wish.
6. Relax and come to a standing position.
7. Repeat as often as you wish. If you are beginning, start with three repetitions and work up to more gradually.

Tai Chi Chuan

> Tai Chi, the primeval force, is like a tree. It grows a trunk and branches, and twigs and flowers and leaves. It grows on and on . . . .
>
> By the time it grows a fruit, there is contained in it the principle which makes it grow on and on. And it will so grow and become once more the primeval force Tai Chi, and there is no stopping it.
>
> Chu Hsi, A.D. 12th century

For centuries Tai Chi has been one of the most widely practiced exercise methods of the Eastern cultures. It is called "The Ultimate Reality" and translated literally, the Chinese word *Tai* means "great," *Chi* means "origin," and *Chuan*, "exercise with the hands."

It is an exercise system that is thought to bring about a harmonious balance of yin and yang. By becoming centered and grounded in the Tai Chi postures, one allows the *Chi* Earth energy to rise into the entire body, just as a tree brings up energy and nourishment from its roots in the soil.

Tai Chi, sometimes called the "thinking man's exercise," is still the mainstay of the exercise movement in China today. One of its unique virtues is that it involves the entire body, all at one time.

All areas of the body are brought into play in a series of specific learned patterns of movement called forms. Tai Chi is characterized by extreme slowness, absolute continuity of movement without breaks or pauses and a concentrated awareness of what one is doing at all times. It flows smoothly from start to finish, and is never interrupted for even a moment.

In China, Tai Chi is practiced every morning as a ritual to prepare the body for the day's activities. When the weather permits, it is usually performed outdoors, which provides the extra benefit of fresh air. To do this exercise at all, it is absolutely essential to be present (in the moment), everything else, eventually, must be excluded. This is why Tai Chi has acquired its reputation as the tranquilizer of the East.

Tai Chi forms transmit the feeling of harmony and rhythm that we usually connect with dance movements. Because the body is balanced at all times, Tai Chi has an extremely harmonizing and calming effect on the body as well as the mind.

The concept of yin and yang is demonstrated throughout the series of Tai Chi exercises. It is a perfect example of movement and quietude. In movement the body opens; in quietude it closes. It is based on the pair of opposites in every aspect of its movement; when there is up, there is down; when there is forward, there is backward; when there is left, there must be right. It includes concentration and at the same time, emptiness.

The inner body, as well as the outer body, is developed by Tai Chi. From familiarity with the exercise forms there comes a gradual realization and understanding of force; and from understanding of force there comes a heightening of the understanding of the body's Ki, both physically and spiritually.

Tai Chi is a form of Qigong (see page 129) and therefore contains all of the three elements contained in all forms of Qigong. *Diaoshen* (the adjustment of posture) is a part of Tai Chi because keeping the spine straight, the head erect, the body balanced from the hips, and the arms empty or relaxed is basic to all of the forms. Diaoxi (controlling or regulating the breath) is part of the more advanced postures or forms. The correct breathing technique, while doing Tai Chi, is to breathe in through the nose and breathe out through the mouth. It is also important to breathe the Ki down into the Dantian (the lower abdomen) for centering and increasing the Ki during the practicing of the forms. Diaoxin (calming the mind) is achieved while engaging in Tai Chi because the mind must be concentrated at all times. For this reason, Tai Chi is often called moving meditation.

The metaphors for the Tai Chi motifs are beautifully evocative as well as kinesthetic: "parting the wild horse's mane, the crane spreads its wings, the hand strums the lute, waving hands like a cloud, embracing the tiger, return to the mountain." All of these postures, and many more, are performed in the relaxed and quiet manner of the discipline with your attention directed toward each movement. The lumbar region is the axis of each movement. Through the practice of Tai Chi the circulation of blood throughout your body, the stimulation of all of the acupuncture/acupressure meridians, and the movement of Ki to every organ and muscle group can easily be accomplished.

Directions for Practicing Tai Chi
- Try to relax into each movement, feel the slow, graceful movements of the form as you move from one position to the next.
- Keep your rate of movement consistent and take deep, regular breaths.

124

- Your center of gravity should always be located in the Dantian. From time to time focus on this center and feel the stability of your body as you rotate around this axis.
- Your knees are your shock absorbers. Use them freely to help you carry your weight lightly and to accentuate the up-and-down movements of each posture.
- Your entire body should feel light and comfortable. If you notice tension building up in your shoulders or arms, just notice it, relax it, and let it go.
- With practice you will begin to experience the Ki energy as it flows through your body. Your fingers will tingle, your hands and feet will become warmer and you will discover an increasing joy and lightness as you progress.
- As you practice, imagine that you are holding a ball of energy in your hands. In each posture and each transition move as if you were lightly holding a medium-sized ball and you will soon discover that, in fact, you can feel the energy as you do the form.
- If possible, when you are learning the form, it would be easier to learn it if you could hear the instructions as you practice. You would enhance your skill and learn more readily if you were to have someone read the following aloud as you go through the form. You might also consider making a tape of the instructions to listen to.

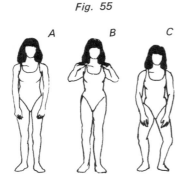

Fig. 55

A B C

Starting Posture

Stand with your weight centered lightly on the balls of your feet, toes pointing comfortably forward and about a shoulder width apart. Before you start to move, relax your arms at your sides, find your center in the Dantian, and let your knees feel springy and loose.

Bend your elbows and raise your arms slowly upward to approximately shoulder height. Just let them float forward with very little effort.

Relax your elbows down toward your sides and let your hands float downward to waist height.

On the downward movement relax your knees and comfortably bend them to accentuate the movement.

Grasp the Bird's Tail, Right and Left

With your weight on your left foot, raise the toes of your right foot and use your right heel to turn your hips to the right.

At the same time, feel that there is a string connecting your right elbow and right knee. As your leg rotates to the right let your right arm accompany it.

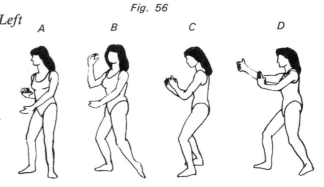

Fig. 56

A B C D

Hold your hand loose and relaxed. Transfer your weight onto your right foot.
Step to your left on your left foot.

Your left elbow and left knee should be aligned as you step so that your arm accompanies the step. As in the preceding posture, your left hand should be above the elbow and very relaxed.

Left Palm to Right Wrist

Again, imagine that your right wrist is aligned with your right knee. Step to your right, place your weight on your right foot and bring the palm of your left hand in line with, but not quite touching, the crease of your right wrist.

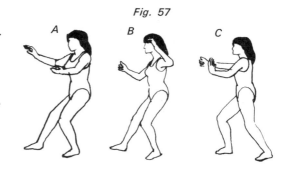

Fig. 57

Shift your weight onto your right leg and move your body forward.

Keep your feet in the same position. Twist your upper body to the left and shift your weight onto your left foot. With the palms of your hands facing each other, circle your arms to the left—loosely down to your left hip, back and forward again in a smooth arc.

As your arms move forward place your left hand gently at the crease of your right wrist.

Smoothly shift your weight forward again onto your right leg.

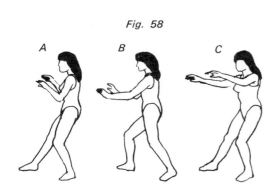

Fig. 58

Roll Back—Press forward

With your feet in the same position, shift your weight onto your left foot and roll back using your arms to accentuate the movement backward. Bring both arms down to your hips and then press the palms of your hands forward and upward.

Shift your weight onto your right foot and press forward. The palms of your hands should press forward as you shift your weight to your right foot.

Single Whip

The Single Whip looks more complicated than it is. Just take it one small increment at a time.

With your weight on your left foot, hold your arms up as if you were saying "stop." Keep them in that position while you do the following:

Slowly turn your body to the left by using your right heel as a pivot. Turn your right foot to the left and bring your arms to the left with your right arm and leg in alignment. This will feel strange at first because your left foot is still pointing

Fig. 59

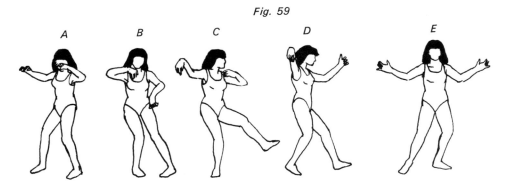

A   B   C   D   E

slightly forward and your right foot is preparing you to turn in the opposite direction from the forward press that you just did.

Keep your left hand in place, still saying "stop." As you slowly shift your weight onto your right foot, bring your right hand next to your left shoulder and gather your fingers and thumb together to form a beak. Slowly move your arm, with the beak, across your chest and out to the right. Fingers pointing out and down.

As your arm moves to the right let it pull the left arm with it. The left hand will end up approximately in front of your right shoulder.

You are now ready to change direction by stepping to the side onto the left foot. Put all of your weight on your right foot, lift your body up to your right, take your left foot off the ground and take a large step to your left. Come down on your left heel and shift your weight to your left leg and foot.

The right arm stays in the beak, still out to the right side as you step and the left arm accompanies the step—elbow and knee aligned as before with the arm bent at the elbow and the palm of your hand facing you.

Fig. 60

Playing the Harp

With your weight still on your left foot and your left arm in the same position as the conclusion of the Single Whip, take a small step forward with your right foot. As you step move your right elbow in line with your right knee. Release the beak as you move and smoothly follow the leg motion of your right leg with a similar motion of your right arm—a slight circle downward and forward. Right heel is on the ground.

Your weight remains on your left leg. Bring your left hand open, palm facing your body, down near your left hip. Your right hand is slightly forward of the left with the palm also facing in. Both elbows are bent. Hold the posture briefly.

Stork Cools Its Wings

Keep your weight on your left foot. The right foot remains with heel on the ground, toes up. Imagine that you have an energy ball between your hands. Carry it in a circle down to your left hip and around until it comes to your left shoulder. The left hand is higher than your right which is closer to your waist. At this point, draw all of your weight onto your left leg and, with a right angle step, bring your right foot next to your left ankle and then, heel down first, step forward onto your right foot. Your right arm stays at your waist, palm up. Your left hand moves from the previous position at your left shoulder, across your face and stops opposite your right shoulder, palm facing away as if you were saying "stop."

Keep your weight on your right foot. Turn to your left and slowly raise your right arm above your head, palm facing your forehead. Bring your left hand, palm facing the ground, down as far as you can.

As your arms move, slide your left foot next to your right foot with just the toes of the left foot touching the ground.

When you are in the completed position, rotate your right hand and press upward.

Brush Push Right and Left

● *With the Right Hand*

With your feet in the same position as the last figure, bring your hands into alignment in front of your waist and comfortably away from your body. Imagine that you are holding the energy ball and bring it as far as you can around to your right.

Step forward with your left heel and bring your left hand forward and down next to your left hip. The right hand stays next to your right shoulder. Start pressing forward onto your left foot and at the same time press forward with your right hand as if you were meeting resistance in the palm of your hand. Stop when your right hand and left knee are diagonally aligned. Most of your weight is forward on your left foot and leg.

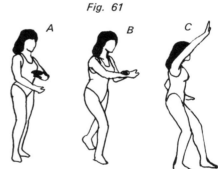

Fig. 61

Take a small step forward with your right leg to bring it closer to your left. Shift your weight onto your right leg and repeat with another brush push to the right.

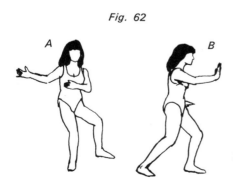

Fig. 62

Simply transfer the energy ball around again to the right with your hands, take a step forward with your left foot, heel down first, and push forward with your right hand as your left hand moves, palm down, to your left side.

● *With the Left Hand*

With your hands still in place from the last brush push, slowly rotate your left foot as far as your can to the left. Use your left heel as a pivot and when you have established your balance on your left foot, swing the energy ball around to your left side, come forward with a large step onto your right foot.

The right arm moves downward next to your waist with the palm down and your left hand pushes forward against an imaginary resistance.

Brush Push Twice with the Right Hand

Pivot to the right with your right foot and add another brush push with your right hand (left leg forward).

Take a small step forward with your right leg to bring it closer to your left. Shift your weight onto your right leg and repeat another brush push to the right (left leg forward).

Pivot and Punch

With your weight still on your left leg and your right hand still pressing forward, pivot on the heel of your left foot as far as you can to the left. At the same time turn your left hand over. It remains at your waist but is now palm up.

Fig. 63

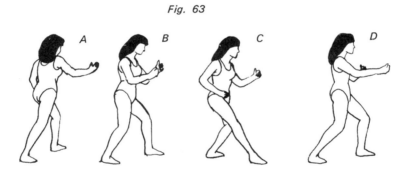

With your weight on your left foot, step forward with your right and place your right hand, palm down, in alignment with your right knee and at waist height.

Form a fist with your right hand. With the weight still on your left foot, raise your right foot in place, turn your foot out to the right as far as possible and place it down and slightly forward.

Keep the fist and place your right elbow in alignment with the right knee.

Step forward onto your left foot.

As you step forward sweep your left arm in front of your waist as if you were holding a large circular ball of energy.

Center your weight evenly between both of your feet.

With your right arm and right fist pierce the energy ball by punching through it, under your left forearm.

Rock back onto your right foot—your left heel is still on the ground for balance—and gather the energy into your Dantian.

Rock forward again onto your left foot and extend your arms forward and upward until they reach your eye level. At that point begin to pivot to the right by bringing the left foot inward. Pivot on your left heel. Your feet are about shoulder width apart.

Pivot and Punch—Conclusion

Continue pivoting to the right until you are facing forward. Let your arms continue to float upward, palms facing outward.

When you are facing forward, sweep the right arm out to the right in a large circle from the top of your head, out from the shoulder and downward and inward toward your waist. As your arm starts to move inward, shift your weight onto your left foot and bring your right foot and arm into alignment as you shift your weight back onto both feet. The right heel comes to rest next to your left heel.

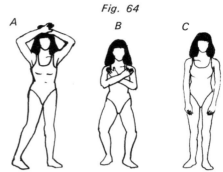
Fig. 64

Just before your feet come together bring your left arm back down in a graceful circle to the left.

Both arms are now at your sides.

Cross your arms at your waist, bring your crossed arms up in front of you. At chest height separate them and let them fall back down.

As your arms descend take a small step to the right with your right foot to become centered and balanced.

Learning Tai Chi

Tai Chi is difficult to learn on your own. We have included a series of pictures and directions from the first section of the yang style of Tai Chi. If this form of exercise piques your interest, we recommend that you look for an experienced teacher to study with.

Fortunately, there are many competent teachers and numerous Tai Chi centers in most North American cities.

In selecting an instructor you should consider the following:
(1) Find a teacher who has been practicing Tai Chi for at least five years and also has had ample experience teaching it.
(2) Select a teacher who is affiliated with a well-established Tai Chi society.

Qigong Exercise

You were first introduced to Qigong (pronounced Cheekung) in the chapter on Breathing. It is a Chinese term applied to many forms of exercise which strengthen Ki energy. Along with deep breathing techniques, the system of Qigong is used to exercise the body's internal systems. These exercises strengthen the internal organs and stimulate the flow of Ki in each of the meridians.

The more precise term for this type of exercise is *Neigong* which means "internal training."

There are countless styles and techniques of Qigong which have been developed throughout China's long history. Of all of these, Tai Chi is perhaps the most well-known in the West.

Another style of Qigong is rapidly gaining in popularity, however. The Crane-style Qigong was begun by Dr. Chao Jing Sian in 1980 in Beijing, China. Since that time its practice has continued to spread for two reasons; one is that it is simpler in form than many of the more elaborate practices. The second is that the results of the practice can be felt sooner and more easily.

In the Orient, especially in China, Korea, and Japan, the crane is a symbol of health and peacefulness. The exercises in this series are based on postures signifying the crane's graceful and harmonious movements.

The Crane-style Qigong
The following postures are structured to allow your internal Ki energy to merge with the energy of the environment.

By performing the following movements your Ki energy is united with the six directions: North, South, East, West, Heaven, and Earth. As you take in the Ki energy of the universe, the flow of Ki in the meridians and internal organs is harmonized with the directional energy which is then stored in the Hara or Dantian (located approximately three inches below your navel). By storing Ki in your lower abdomen your energy is raised and your metabolism is enhanced and balanced.

This is the first section of the Crane-style Qigong. There are six additional sections to learn if you wish to continue your practice further.

- *Suggestions for Your Practice*
1. All your movements should be in a circular pattern with soft and flexible motions.
2. Focus your eyes on a distant object to improve your concentration.
3. Your muscles should be controlled but not strained.
4. Your clothing should be loose and comfortable.
5. Practice in a beautiful natural setting or on a mat that is made of natural materials if possible.
6. Let your mind follow the direction and flow of the Ki energy. In the first part you are sending it outward to attract the energy of the six directions. You then bring it back through the crown chakra and down into your Dantian.

Qigong   *Fig. 65*

Preparation
Stand naturally, facing south with your feet placed shoulder width apart. Rest your arms at your sides. Throughout all of the exercises let your tongue remain on the upper palate inside your mouth just behind the teeth. This allows the Ki energy to circulate in a full orbit. Stand as if you were a graceful crane and let your Ki energy flow from the crown chakra to the Dantian in your lower abdomen.

1

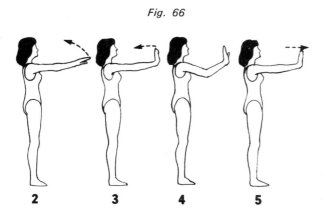

Fig. 66

Raising the Wings
Guide the Ki from your abdomen down the front of your body and around to your spine. Feel it travel up your spine to a point between your shoulders. Next, direct it through your arms to the palms of your hands. With your palms facing downward, slowly raise your arms up and forward to shoulder level. Turn your hands upward to a 90 degree angle with your fingers and palms facing forward. In this position slowly push outward and retract softly three times.

This movement serves to unite your energy with that of the south. Its purpose is to open the point in the palms of your hands to allow the internal Ki to draw in the external Ki.

Breathing:
- Inhale as you raise your arms.
- Exhale as you turn your hands upward.
- Exhale as you push forward.
- Inhale as you retract your hands.

Opening the Wings
Loosen your wrists and open your arms to the sides at shoulder level. Turn your hands upward again to a 90 degree angle with your palms facing east and west. Push forward and retract as before, three times.

This motion is to unite your energy with that of the east and west.

Breathing:
- Exhale as you push forward.
- Inhale as you retract your arms.

Fig. 67

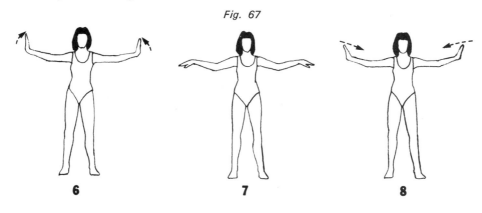

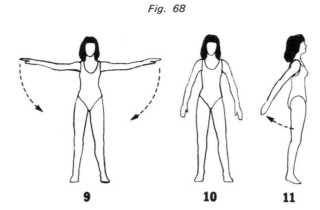

Fig. 68

9   **10**   **11**

Closing the Wings

Bring your arms down close to, but not touching your sides. Push them back about 45 degrees, hands turned out and raise your heels out. This movement brings Ki to your fingers and begins to separate negative and positive Ki.

Breathing:
• Do the movement in one slow inhalation.

Fig. 69

12   **13**

Contorting the Wings

With your arms in the same position, bend your wrists and form a claw with each hand. Next, rapidly move your hands forward, close to your ribs, and open your hands, palms up. As you do the arm movement, lower your heels force-fully with your knees bent.

This position, along with Closing the Wings, unites your Ki energy with that of the north. It also expels negative Ki. Positive Ki enters as your heels hit the ground and begins to circulate in a smooth circle around your body.

Breathing:
• Exhale throughout the entire movement.

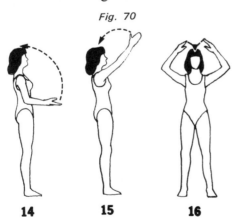

Fig. 70

14   **15**   **16**

Guiding Ki from Hands to Head

Slowly raise your arms with the palms of your hands facing upward. Imagine that you are holding a large balloon. Continue raising your arms until the palms of your hands are facing the top of your head. Concentrate on sending the Ki energy from the palms of your hands into the crown chakra at the top of your head.

This movement is a preparation for the next one in which your energy unites with that of Heaven.

Breathing:
• Inhale as you raise your arms.
• Transfer the Ki from your hands to your head by exhaling.

Uniting with Heaven

Interlace your fingers and bring the palms of your hands closer to the top of your head. Next, turn your palms upward, fingers still interlaced, and push upward. The upward motion should come from your whole body. Return your arms and hands to the original (palms down) position again as you bend your knees. Keeping your knees bent, let your head rotate gently from left to right and back again three times. Again, straighten your legs and push your palms upward as far as you can stretch. After the stretch, keep your hands in the same position, relax your arms and bend your knees and lean forward from the waist. Starting from left to right, let your upper body swing from side to side, slowly and gently. Repeat the upward stretch and the body swaying motions another time if you wish.

Fig. 71

17

The palms turned upward receive the energy from Heaven and bring it back into your body as you sway from side to side. Return to an upright position with your hands still over your head.

Breathing:
- Inhale as you interlace your fingers just above your head.
- Exhale as you push upward.
- Breathe naturally when you sway from side to side.

Uniting with the Earth

With your fingers still interlaced, bend forward and push your hands downward in the center (palms down). Bend your knees slightly if you find this more comfortable. Raise your hands up to the level of your knees and then push down to the left. Raise up again and then push down to the right.

This movement integrates your Ki energy with that of the Earth.

Fig. 72

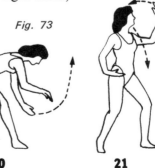

18

Breathing:
- Exhale as you bend forward and push down.
- Inhale as you raise your arms and push up.

Return of Ki (Part 1)

Separate your hands and transfer your weight onto your right leg. As you slowly return to an upright position, bring your right hand, palm turned up, slightly below your waist. Simultaneously step forward with your left foot and raise your left hand, palm turned inward and fingers pointing up, to just above your eye level. Turn your head and eyes to look at the palm of your left hand. Return your head to the center and raise your left hand over the top

Fig. 73

19   **20**   **21**

Fig. 74

22

of your head. Imagine the Ki energy flowing from the palm of your hand into the crown chakra. As you slowly exhale send the energy from your hand into the top of your head.

Inhale as your crown chakra receives the energy. Repeat the exhalation and inhalation three times.

Next, bring your left hand down, palm facing down and your fingers nearly touching your left ear, to the same level as your right hand.

Change the center of gravity to place your weight onto your left leg and repeat the exercise on the right side.

Breathing:
- Inhale as you raise your left hand.
- Exhale as you turn your head to look at your left hand.
- Inhale as you place your left hand above your head.
- Exhale as you send the energy from your hand into the top of your head.
- Inhale as the chakra opens to receive it.

Fig. 75

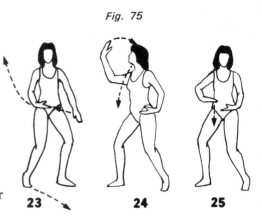

23   **24**   **25**

Fig. 76

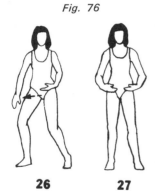

26   **27**

Return of Ki (Part 2)
Shift your weight onto the right leg and bring your left leg forward so that your feet are shoulder width apart and your knees slightly bent. With your palms facing downward, bring your arms back slightly behind your body. Next, with your elbows slightly bent, bring them to the center of your body in front of the Dantian. Turn the fingertips of each hand so that they are facing each other. Remain in this position while taking several deep breaths.

This motion returns the Ki to the Dantian.

Breathing:
- Exhale and inhale gently as you wish.
- After a period of practice, the Ki in every part of your body will intermingle and harmonize, promoting a more balanced energy state and a more vigorous body.

Dō-In

Dō-In has its origins in the ancient traditions of the East but is currently being practiced in the East and West alike. These centuries-old exercises have been thought to be the origin of Yoga, the martial arts and many other methods of self-development.

These exercises can be practiced without special training. They are of benefit for balancing the body and raising energy levels as well as for attaining a higher degree of spirituality.

THE MARTIAL ARTS

In all of the martial arts the essence of *budō* (the martial ways) lies in its spirit. Whether participating in Karate, Judo, the Chinese Kung-Fu or any other form of martial art, one must strive to gain self-mastery and control before attempting to control others. To this end the martial arts are centered about the premise that overcoming an adversary is possible only through proper alignment with the universal force or energy.

Aikido

Within the martial arts system the *budō* of Aikidō stands out as a way to go beyond the disciplines of force and technique to an alignment with the natural laws of the universe.

Aikidō means "The way to union with Ki" or the "way to harmony of the Spirit." It was founded in the early 1900s by Morihei Ueshiba and was originally called Aiki-Budō or the *budō* of unification and oneness. The founder's goal was to reconcile aggression with love. His statement of philosophy includes the following:

> If you shut your eyes you see nothing. If you leave out your ego and your self-desire, the whole universe will be yours. Aiki is such an assimilation of spiritual ways.

He also stated that:

> Aiki is the expression of Truth itself. It is the way of calling people together and reconciling them with love whenever they may attack us.

The distinguishing characteristic of Aikidō is that instead of seeing an opponent as an aggressor he is seen through the egoless "Realm of No-self" taking the flow of the opponent's Ki and deflecting an attack by sending that energy back rather than confronting and absorbing it directly.

Aikidō is closely aligned with the art of Japanese swordsmanship, *Kendō*. The tip of the little finger to the elbow is considered the "handblade" or *tegatana* which is directed by "Breath Power," *kokyū-ryoku*, flowing from the center of the body. When accompanied by proper body movements, *tai-sabaki*, there is a powerful extension of Ki from the lungs into the handblades. The original direction and force of the attack are magnified instead of resisted and the attacker is led rather than forced into submission.

In Aikidō correct body movement is seen to be similar to that of a rapidly spinning top. A major goal is to involve an opponent in turning around your center axis. This movement allows you to guide your adversary at will, just as a spinning top throws off anything that touches it. Also, a top, when spinning, is stable. Therefore, if an opponent applies pressure from any angle and you do not collide with it but instead turn with the direction of the force, the power instantly returns to the attacker who must then deal with it.

This usually results in loss of balance for the one who initiated the attack.

Aikidō may be practiced by everyone regardless of size or age. Rather than depending on strength or force, the student of Aikidō is trained to concentrate on skills that unite mind and body. The mind is seen to work best when it is calmly focused at the Dantian or "one point," three inches below the navel, while the body movements become fluid and natural when all stress and tension have been released.

Basic Introduction to Aikidō

The following practices will give you a practical understanding of how using the basic Aikidō principles can increase your Ki energy.

Standing Posture

The typical Aikidō unified standing posture places one foot in front of the other at right angles. To find this posture do the following:

1. Stand erect and place the heel of your right foot close to the instep of your left foot.
2. Take a comfortable step forward and slightly flex your knees. You are now in a relaxed and comfortable position and your upper body is slightly turned which narrows the possibility of a direct attack. This stance also permits rapid movement in any direction.

    If your right foot is forward it is called *the right oblique stance* and if your left foot is forward it is called *the left oblique stance*.

    Your entire body should be held without tension in the form of a triangle with your right arm forward (in the right oblique stance), slightly above your waist, fingers apart and hand held as if for clapping. Both of your elbows should be comfortably bent with your left arm placed to the left side, lower than your right. Both wrists should be flexed.

Distance

Ideal distance or *ma-ai* is most important in Aikidō as space is needed to maneuver easily and safely. *Ma-ai* is a distance at which you can maintain calmness without feeling anxiety or threatened by an opponent. Maintaining this safe distance under attack is an important principle of Aikidō technique. It is a distance at which your opponent cannot touch you without making a major body movement.

In *ma-ai* you are able to see your opponent using peripheral vision. Peripheral vision becomes narrowed through fear or anger. As Aikidō training teaches you to remain calm under attack you learn that it is not necessary to directly look at something to see it clearly. You learn to see things as a unified whole.

Concentration on the "One Point"

Just as a spinning top must maintain one small center of gravity to continue in motion, your success in extending Ki into all of your actions depends upon your ability to focus your mind at your center or "one point."

In Aikidō, as you learn to move with your mind focused at the Dantian, you begin to extend power smoothly from your center into every part of your body. This allows you to be steady and stable in mind and body with your energy flowing outward in a steady stream that will be manifest in all of your movements.

The following exercises will enable you and a partner to experience "extending Ki." They are based upon the premise that the weight of the entire body must always be centered at the "one point." In Aikidō it is said that the immovable mind makes an immovable body. Therefore, the "one point" in the lower abdomen is a place to focus the mind.

Exercise 1 (To be done barefoot.)

In a standing position, increase the strength in any part of your body. You might, for example increase the tension in your legs or back.

Have your partner push your left shoulder. You will easily be thrown out of balance and alignment.

Next, stand naturally on your toes, feet parallel, shoulder width apart. Feel all of your upper body weight as it settles naturally at a point about three inches below your navel.

Keep this state and slowly lower your heels to the floor without moving your weight backward.

Concentrate on the "one point" imagining that it is the exact center of the universe.

Have your partner push your shoulder again and experience the difference in your strength and the body's resistance.

Exercise 2

Stand in a comfortable position and extend your dominant arm using as much power and energy as you can to keep your partner from bending it upward from the elbow. You will find that, with little effort, your arm can be bent by your partner.

Raise up on your toes and center your body as in Exercise 1. Focus on the "one point" which is your center of gravity and the place to focus your strength and power.

Extend your arm again while feeling your energy flowing from the "one point" up through your arm and out your fingers. Relax your shoulders and arms and visualize them as a clear channel for your energy.

Have your partner attempt to bend your arm in the same way as before. You will be surprised at your increased strength. When you learn to concentrate your power and extend it outward you will discover additional strength and a source of abundant energy.

Exercise 3

This exercise will allow you to see the benefit of extending Ki into all situations. By learning to project your Ki energy forward you can begin to experience the unification of mind and body.

When you are going to a place that you wish to go, your Ki energy is projected forward in pleasant expectation. The same feeling can consciously be evoked to accomplish any task that you undertake.

Have your partner stand several feet in front of you and slightly to the side.

Walk forward at normal speed and have your partner raise his or her arm, using the hand farthest away from you for the best leverage.

Your partner should attempt to stop you by reaching across your body and gently grasping your opposite shoulder. You will feel the resistance and most likely will experience enough discomfort to stop.

Repeat the exercise with the exception that, before you start to walk, establish a sense of expectation. Pretend that you are anxious to go to meet someone you care for or are going to a favorite place.

If you extend your Ki strongly your partner's resistance will not impede your progress and will hardly be felt.

Exercise 4

This exercise is done without a partner and is meant to give you a sense of Aikidō movement in which your breath is coordinated with the united force of your mind and body. The power which is exerted from the whole body acting in concert is called *kokyū-ryoku* or Breath Power.

Stand comfortably with your feet placed about shoulder width apart, arms at your sides. Take a deep breath and concentrate your energy at the "one point." (Use the centering technique in Exercise 1 if you wish.) Imagine your lower arms and hands as handblades, wrists flexed, and swing them up and outward to a position level with your eyes as you step into a right oblique stance. (Right foot forward and at right angles to your left.) Exhale forcefully and completely as you raise your arms.

Center your weight over your left foot keeping your balance securely over your hips.

Change your direction 180 degrees to the left by pivoting on your left foot and facing completely to the left. While turning, move your hands down in a sweeping motion and then swing them up as you step out again on your right foot in the other direction.

Continue at your own pace changing directions while adding the breathing and arm movements.

When you have mastered this exercise, change to the other side by leading with your left foot and pivoting with your right.

In Aikidō, as you were able to discover by performing Exercise 4, the continuous and flexible motion based at the hips is like the performing of a dance. It is a graceful spherical motion. When you study Aikidō, you learn to coordinate each movement with your breath and unify your entire body into a systematically controlled whole of mind, body, and spirit.

The Founder, Morihei Ueshiba has stated:

The secret of Aikidō is to harmonize ourselves with the movement of the universe and bring ourselves into accord with the universe itself. He who has gained the secret of Aikidō has the universe in himself and can say, "I am the universe."

For additional information contact:

The United States Aikidō Federation
142 W. Eighteenth St.
New York, N.Y. 10011

Yoga

The Sun Salutation

This is a Yoga breathing and stretching exercise that relaxes and energizes your mind and body. It is especially good to use in the morning because it stimulates all of your body systems.

The Sun Salutation or *Surya Namaskar*, the Sanskrit term, is a graceful sequence of twelve positions performed as one continuous exercise. Each position counteracts the one before because it stretches your body in a different way. It alternately expands and contracts your chest which aids your breathing.

Practiced often it will stretch your spine and tendons, help you to breathe more deeply, and provide steady, moderate exercise for your heart.

If you do not have time to learn a complete Yoga program, you can derive great benefit from doing the Sun Salutation. It can be done as a complete exercise in and of itself.

One round consists of two sequences, the first leading with your right foot, and the second leading with your left.

When you are beginning, it is best to learn the body movements and then add the breathing sequence when you are ready. Start with a comfortable number of repetitions and gradually increase until you can do ten.

Position 1—Exhale
Stand erect with your feet together. Put your palms together in front of your chest. Relax your body before you begin.

Position 2—Inhale
Raise both of your arms, stretching them back over your head. Arch your back

Fig. 77

and let your head go as far back as you can. Imagine yourself stretching in the sun's rays and receiving its warmth and energy.

Position 3—Exhale
Bend forward, touching your hands to the floor in front of your feet. Bend your knees slightly if you wish.

Let your head hang down and be relaxed. As you breathe out, empty your lungs and pull your stomach up.

Position 4—Inhale

Move your right leg back, letting your right knee touch the floor. Place your hands parallel with your feet. Your left knee will be bent forward and your left foot will be flat on the ground. Stretch your head and back in a backward arch while you look up as far as you can.

Position 5—Exhale

Bring your left leg back and support your weight on your hands and toes. Keep your head and body in a straight line and look at the floor between your hands.

Position 6—Hold your breath out

Lower your knees, chest, and forehead, keeping your hips up and your toes curled under.

Position 7—Inhale

Lower your hips, point your toes, and stretch back as far as you can. Keep your legs together and shoulders down. Hips should be on or close to the mat. Bend your elbows if you wish. Look up.

Position 8—Exhale

Turn your toes under, raise your hips and pivot into an inverted "V." Place your heels on or as close to the mat as they will stretch. Keep your head down and your shoulders back.

Position 9—Inhale

Step forward and place your left foot between your hands. You may initially have to place your hands in line with your foot for proper alignment. Rest your right knee on the floor and look up.

Position 10—Exhale

Bring your left leg forward and bend forward from the waist down. Touch your hands to the floor beside your feet. Bend your knees slightly if you wish.

Position 11—Inhale

Stretch your arms forward, then up and back over your head. Bend back from the waist. Let your head go as far back as you can.

Position 12—Exhale

Bring your hands down to your chest as you come back to a standing position.

Special Considerations

You should wear comfortable clothing when you do the Sun Salutation.

After you have memorized the positions, do them a little faster so that you will be stimulating your breathing and heart rate.

After you become familiar with the postures and the breathing, concentrate on greeting the sun or your environment. At the conclusion of the exercise you will experience a feeling of centeredness and harmony.

If you are not in good physical health do this exercise with care and stop if you feel severe discomfort.

Rocking the Spine

In Japan this exercise is known as *Kōhō-Tentō-Undō* and is considered to be a powerful way to extend Ki energy. It is also often included in most Yoga programs.

Rocking the spine is beneficial for limbering your spine, inverting blood flow and is an excellent exercise for toning your entire body.

Caution: If you have back problems of any kind do not attempt this exercise unless you check with your physician first.

Starting Position
Sit on the floor. Clasp your arms around your knees or sit cross-legged and hold onto your ankles or toes. Keep your knees bent throughout the exercise.

Fig. 78

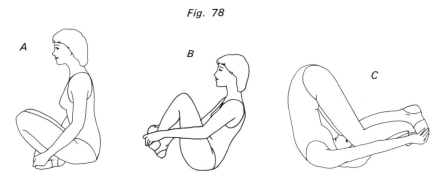

Instructions
Holding your initial position, roll backward as far as you comfortably can. Keep your chin tucked toward your chest and your back slightly rounded.

Maintaining your momentum, roll forward to a seated position. Repeat five to seven times maintaining a gentle rocking motion.

Breathing:
• Inhale in the starting position.
• Exhale while rocking backward.
• Inhale while rocking forward.

Cat Stretch

This is a well-known Yoga exercise that stretches the back and also tones the muscles of the neck, shoulders, abdomen, and spine. It also aids in spinal flexibility.

The Cat Stretch or *Marjariasana* (the Sanskrit term) is done slowly and gracefully.

Starting Position
Rest your weight on your hands and knees.

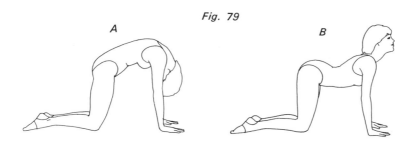

Fig. 79

Instructions
Take a deep breath as you sag in the middle and raise your head. Slowly exhale as you lower your head and arch your back. Repeat for five repetitions. Hold each posture as long as you wish.

Leg Pulls

The Sanskrit term for this exercise is *Supta Padasana*. It is a Yoga exercise that is beneficial for firming your abdomen, buttocks, and thighs. It also limbers the leg muscles and stretches the spine.

Starting Position
Lie on your back, arms relaxed at your sides.

Fig. 80

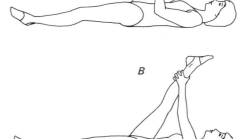

Instructions
Bend your right leg and pull it close to your body. Be sure that your left leg is extended in a straight line from your hips to your toes.

Raise your right leg when your leg is fully extended, pull your foot gently back toward your head.

Slowly return to your original position.

Alternating legs, repeat five times to each side.

Breathe deeply as you stretch.

Recently, there has been a growing interest in these forms of exercise in the West. If you wish to further your understanding of the Eastern exercise systems we recommend you turn to the suggested reading section at the end of this book.

Relaxation

The Western Concept

Deep relaxation contributes to a sense of well-being and high energy by counter-acting the stresses and tensions in your life. The word "relaxation" comes from the Latin *laxare*, which means "to loosen, slacken, or soften." As you already know, stress is not something that comes from the outside. It is, instead, a condition that you produce internally, of which you might not be completely aware. For example, when you lie down to rest or to sleep, your muscles may continue to carry a certain residual tension. Often this tension is unnoticed but it still can be a constant drain of your energy reserves. A useful corollary to this, however, is that if you create tension, you can also learn to control it with relaxation training. Therefore, while it may be difficult to control the amount of stress you experience each day, it is possible to control your response to that stress. Once you start to observe and voluntarily let go of your tensions, the process of relaxation will become more and more automatic which, in turn, will allow you to begin to use your body in a more efficient way.

A scientific definition of deep relaxation involves the complete absence of neuro-muscular activity and includes the most beneficial kind of rest and replenishment for your mind and body. This type of relaxation can be developed through the repeated use of several very interesting and well-established techniques which we have included in this chapter. With just a small amount of time and practice you will be able to attain a state of deep relaxation whenever and wherever you wish.

By understanding how stress and tensions undermine your health and energy, you will be better able to choose the relaxation skills that will be the most beneficial for you to practice.

How You React to Stress

Stress is experienced by everyone throughout the course of every day. It is a normal physiological response in your body to a stimulus called a *stressor*. A stressor can be real or imaginary and, in either case, causes a physical reaction to occur.

The definitions of *stress* are: Any stimulus that disturbs your mind-body balance and harmony, the demand to adapt to different situations or conditions, and antici-pation of a demand or threat. Stress offers challenges and stimuli to make life interesting. Many experts feel that stress is a learning experience that can enable growth and development to occur.

Stress only becomes a problem when your body's "fight or flight" stress response continues long after the real threat is gone. Repeated occurrences of stressful condi-tions often cause an alteration in your body chemistry which can finally result in chronic fatigue and illness.

It is estimated by some studies that today we experience as much stress in one day as our ancestors experienced in one year. The caveman was always using his body in a way that allowed him to survive in a hostile environment. Today, a body stimulated for "fight or flight" is like a car that is being run twenty-four hours a day at full speed. The parts of the body or car cannot withstand such severe treatment and eventually function is impaired.

The stress response begins when your central nervous system registers a demand on your physical and emotional resources. When you experience excessive noise, an overcrowded freeway or any of the hundreds of uncomfortable situations or conditions that can occur, the first stage of your stress response, known as the *alarm stage*, goes into action.

This stage is characterized by a surge of energy supplied by your adrenal glands and the sympathetic, or energy expending, branch of your nervous system. Your sympathetic system, which controls involuntary functions such as digestion, and heart and breath rate, sends alarm signals throughout your body, while your adrenals pour the hormone adrenalin into your blood to increase your available energy.

Nature seems to have designed this first stage with the intent that it should suffice for handling most of the everyday demands that you might face. The alarm stage is known as the *fight-or-flight reaction* because it brings about a massive mobilization of energy. It helps to fuel your excitement in a pleasurable situation and your anger in a frustrating one. If you have to move quickly to avoid a harmful situation, the alarm response provides the necessary burst of energy.

After the demanding situation has passed, your physical-emotional system automatically seeks rest in order to restore inner balance and peace. If the external demand remains, or if you continue to trigger the stress response through worry or frustration, you soon enter the *stage of resistance*. At this point, your body further mobilizes itself for longer-term battle against the stressor. The resistance stage is necessary to help you survive prolonged physical hardship such as illness or injury but if it cannot be turned off within a reasonable length of time, it becomes chronic and its biochemical effects can erode the foundations of your energy and well-being.

When prolonged high levels of adrenalin, along with signals from the hypothalamus (a small master control center in your brain), activate the pituitary gland, a number of reactions occur. Your pituitary gland secretes hormones that mobilize your whole physical-emotional system for long-term battle. One of these hormones raises your blood pressure by causing your arteries to narrow. Another stimulates your thyroid gland which accelerates your metabolism while other hormones raise your blood sugar level, and alter your immune system.

This stage of stress response is not damaging, however, it can give way to the *stage of exhaustion* if the stress continues to build. Should you remain tense and are therefore unable to allow the second stage to decrease, fatigue will persist and serious damage can ensue as you enter the third stage.

The mechanics of the stage of exhaustion are complex but the principal effects include: chronic elevation of your blood pressure, tearing of your arterial walls and elevation of clotting elements in your blood, increases in blood sugar levels, and lowered resistance to disease, increased stomach acidity, increased inflammation in your joints and hyperactivity of your whole system, resulting in chronic fatigue and insomnia. All of the above accelerate the aging process, sap your vitality, and make you more susceptible to serious illness.

The Social Readjustment Rating Scale

Although stresses affect each individual uniquely, their relative importance is remarkably uniform. Two American researchers, Thomas Holmes and Richard Rahe, have developed a questionnaire, called the Social Readjustment Rating Scale, designed to measure the impact of various common "life events" on your health and well-being. There are forty-three specific life events listed and each one carries a certain weight expressed in *Life Change Units* (LCUs). At the top of the scale is "Death of a Spouse," which carries 100 LCUs. In the center is "Mariage" (a positive event) worth 50 LCUs, and at the bottom of the list are "Minor Violations of the Law" worth 11 LCUs. Holmes and Rahe have found a direct correlation between high LCU scores and increased chances of major health problems within the following two years.

Scoring Guidelines
0—150=one chance in three of a major health problem in the next two years
150—300=50/50 chance of a major health problem in the next two years
300+=90 percent chance of a major health problem in the next two years

Life Event	*Mean Value*
Family:	
Death of spouse or a child	100 —
Divorce	73 —
Marital separation	65 —
Death of close family member	63 —
Marriage	50 —
Marital reconciliation	45 —
Major change in health of family	44 —
Pregnancy	40 —
Addition of new family member	39 —
Major change in arguments with wife	35 —
Son or daughter leaving home	29 —
In-law troubles	29 —
Wife starting or ending work	26 —
Major change in family get-togethers	15 —
Personal:	
Detention in jail	63 —
Major personal injury or illness	53 —
Sexual difficulties	39 —
Death of a close friend	37 —
Outstanding personal achievement	28 —
Start or end of formal schooling	26 —
Major change in living conditions	25 —
Major revision of personal habits	24 —
Change to a new school	20 —
Change in residence	20 —
Major change in recreation	19 —
Major change in church activities	19 —
Major change in sleeping habits	16 —
Major change in eating habits	15 —
Vacation	13 —
Christmas	12 —
Minor violations of the law	11 —
Work:	
Being fired from work	47 —
Retired from work	45 —
Major business adjustment	39 —
Change to different line of work	36 —
Major change in work responsibilities	29 —
Trouble with boss	23 —
Major change in working conditions	20 —
Financial:	
Major change in financial state	38 —
Mortgage or loan over $20,000	31 —
Mortgage foreclosure	30 —
Mortgage or loan less than $20,000	17 —
Total	—

Becoming Aware of Stress

Most of us think of stress as the necessary price we must pay for living in a complex society, being productive and creative and pushing our physical and emotional resources to the limit. We often ignore many stress warning signals. However, ignored stresses pile up and so do the physical and emotional effects of stress. By using the following checklist you can discover whether or not you are ignoring the symptoms of stress in your life. If you answer yes to more than three of the following, you should begin to focus on the many ways that are available to you for dealing with stress in a creative and specific manner.

Stress Warning Signals
(Check the responses that apply to you.)

Feeling unable to slow down and relax	—
Explosive anger in response to minor irritation	—
Anxiety or tension lasting more than a few days	—
Feeling that things frequently go wrong	—
Inability to focus attention	—
Frequent or prolonged feelings of boredom	—
Fatigue	—
Sexual problems	—
Sleep disturbances	—
Tension headaches	—
Migraine headaches	
Cold hands or feet	
Aching neck and shoulder muscles	—
Indigestion	—
Menstrual distress	—
Nausea or vomiting	—
Loss of appetite	—
Diarrhea	—
Ulcers	—
Heart palpitations	—
Constipation	—
Lower back pain	—
Allergy or asthma attacks	—
Shortness of breath	—
Frequent colds	—
Frequent low-grade infections	—
Frequent minor accidents	—
Overeating	—
Increased consumption of alcohol	—
Increased dependence on drugs	—

Stress without Distress

When everything is going well, you experience the absence of the stress warning signals plus much more. Your life then feels balanced and whole and you are productive but not driven, aroused but not anxious, perhaps physically or emotionally tired from time to time but still able to experience complete rest and recovery. You are also energetic and optimistic.

Hans Selye, who first documented the stress response more than three decades ago, wrote in his book *Stress without Distress*, that stress itself is not the problem; the problem is our attitude toward stress-producing situations. He concluded that, properly channeled, stress is necessary. Without some good action, there is no worthwhile challenge. The trick is to meet the challenges sensibly and effectively.

Signs of Successfully Coping with Stress
(Check the responses that apply to you.)

Ability to carry out jobs efficiently —
Ability to take responsibility —
Ability to work effectively under authority,
   rules, difficulties, and limits —
Tolerance of frustration —
Ability to adapt to changes —
Reliability —
Sense of belonging —
Tolerance of others —
Ability to show friendliness and love —
Ability to enjoy recreation —
Sense of humor —
Self-direction —
Reasonable sense of independence and self-reliance —
Sense of fulfillment —
Ability to easily relax and sleep —

Stress Reduction Techniques

Deep relaxation is attained by a process which is described as "passive volition" or "passive concentration," which involves gently focusing your awareness upon specific physiological cues or mental images, without active willing. This leads to a state of extreme sensitivity to internal physical and mental messages, and heightened self-awareness.

Relaxation training requires daily practice, just as any physical skill does. Over time, with regular practice, you will be able to relax, within a few seconds, anytime you wish.

Suggestions for Your Practice
- Keep all external stimuli to a minimum.
- Choose a quiet room where you will not be disturbed.
- Be sure that the room temperature is comfortable.

- If possible, avoid bright light in the room.
- Wear loose, comfortable clothing.
- Sit in a comfortable chair with your head, back, arms, and legs well supported or lie down with your head supported and your legs not touching, toes relaxed and pointing outward. Arms resting comfortably at your sides.

Autogenics

Autogenic Training is a systematic program that will teach your body and mind to respond quickly and effectively to your verbal commands to relax and return to a balanced, normal state. It is one of the most effective and comprehensive ways to reduce chronic stress.

This system was first taught by Johannes H. Schultz, a Berlin psychiatrist, whose research focused on the most effective relaxation techniques found in hypnosis and Yoga. In 1932 he published his findings in a book titled *Autogenic Training*.

In its present form, Autogenics allows you to induce a feeling of warmth and heaviness throughout your body by reversing the "fight or flight" state of stress. It has six parts that can be mastered at a slow but steady pace. The first part includes the theme of heaviness which promotes relaxation of the voluntary muscles in your body. These are the muscles over which you have complete control. The second part brings about the relaxation of the smooth muscles which, among other functions, control the diameter of the blood vessels in your extremities. This allows your hands and feet to become warm and heavy as an increase of warming blood is allowed to flow away from your trunk and head, where it immediately goes during times of stress. The third part normalizes your heart rate, the fourth calms your respiratory system, the fifth relaxes and warms your abdomen and the sixth reduces the flow of blood to your head. Each part has a key phrase which triggers a relaxation response.

Instructions

Each exercise will introduce a verbal formula that you will constantly repeat over and over to yourself. When you are ready to stop, say to yourself, "when I open my eyes, I will feel refreshed and alert." Then, slowly open your eyes, breathe a few deep breaths and stretch and flex your arms and legs.

Heaviness Theme

Week 1

Repeat the following verbal formulas for one and a half minutes, five to eight times a day. Say the formula slowly, taking about five seconds, then pause about three seconds. Repeat each phrase about four times. Always begin with your dominant arm. (If you write with your right hand, begin with your right arm.)

My right arm is heavy.
My left arm is heavy.
Both of my arms are heavy.

If you have difficulty with achieving a sensation of heaviness, you may want to add visual imagery. For example, you might imagine weights attached to your arms and legs gently pulling them down.

Week 2
Repeat the following verbal formulas for three minutes, four to seven times a day:

> *My right arm is heavy.*
> *My left arm is heavy.*
> *Both of my arms are heavy.*
> *My right leg is heavy.*
> *My left leg is heavy.*
> *Both of my legs are heavy.*
> *My arms and legs are heavy.*

Week 3
Repeat the following for four minutes, four to seven times a day:

> *My right arm is heavy.*
> *My left arm is heavy.*
> *Both of my arms are heavy.*
> *Both of my legs are heavy.*
> *My arms and legs are heavy.*

Warmth Theme

Week 4
Repeat the following for five minutes, four to seven times a day:

> *My right arm is heavy.*
> *My left arm is heavy.*
> *My arms and legs are heavy.*
> *My right arm is warm.*
> *My left arm is warm.*
> *Both of my arms are warm.*

Week 5
Repeat the following for eight minutes, three to six times a day:

> *My right arm is heavy.*
> *My left arm is heavy.*
> *My arms and legs are heavy.*
> *My right arm is warm.*
> *My left arm is warm.*

My right leg is warm.
My left leg is warm.
Both of my legs are warm.
My arms and legs are warm.

Week 6
Repeat the following for ten to fifteen minutes, three to six times a day:

My right arm is heavy.
My left arm is heavy.
My arms and legs are heavy.
Both of my arms are warm.
Both of my legs are warm.
My arms and legs are warm.
My arms and legs are heavy and warm.

Week 7
Repeat the following for ten to twenty minutes, three to six times a day:

My right arm is heavy.
My left arm is heavy.
My arms and legs are heavy.
My arms and legs are warm.
My arms and legs are heavy and warm.

If you have trouble experiencing a feeling of warmth using the verbal formulas, try visual imagery. For instance, you might imagine yourself in a warm bath with the warmth of the water all around you.

Practice the rest of the exercises for ten to twenty minutes, one to six times a day. Remember to move at your own pace.

Heartbeat Theme

Week 8
If you have trouble becoming aware of your heartbeat, lie on your back with your right hand resting over your heart. If you experience any discomfort or distress while doing this exercise, move on to the next three themes and do this one in week eleven.

My right arm is heavy.
My left arm is heavy.
My arms and legs are heavy and warm.
My heartbeat is calm and regular.

Breathing Theme

Week 9
This enhances the tendency of the previous themes to slow and deepen respiration.

> *My right arm is heavy and warm.*
> *My left arm is heavy and warm.*
> *My arms and legs are heavy and warm.*
> *My heartbeat is calm and regular.*
> *It breathes me.*

Solar Plexus Theme

Week 10
Skip this exercise if you have ulcers, diabetes, or any condition involving bleeding from abdominal organs.

> *My right arm is heavy and warm.*
> *My left arm is heavy and warm.*
> *My arms and legs are heavy and warm.*
> *My heartbeat is calm and regular.*
> *It breathes me.*
> *My solar plexus is warm.*

Forehead Theme

Week 11
It is best to do this exercise lying on your back.

> *My right arm is heavy and warm.*
> *My left arm is heavy and warm.*
> *My arms and legs are heavy and warm.*
> *My heartbeat is calm and regular.*
> *It breathes me.*
> *My solar plexus is warm.*
> *My forehead is cool.*

Autogenics—The Short Form

After mastering the longer technique, many people have gained a lasting state of deep relaxation by using the following suggestions. This is possible because the phrases act as triggers to bring about the naturally occurring relaxation processes in your body that have been activated through your continued practice.

Instructions
- Begin with your dominant arm and leg.
- Cultivate a passive, casual attitude.
- Make a mental contact with each part of your body and maintain a steady (verbal or visual) image of the phrase in the mind.

Autosuggestion phrases:
"My right arm is heavy." Repeat five to six times.
"I am at peace."

"My left arm is heavy." Repeat five to six times.
"I am at peace."

"My right leg is heavy." Repeat five to six times.
"I am at peace."

"My left leg is heavy." Repeat five to six times.
"I am at peace."

"My arms and legs are heavy and warm." Repeat five to six times.
"I am at peace."

"My heartbeat is calm and regular." Repeat five to six times.
"I am at peace."

"My breathing is calm and regular." Repeat five to six times.
"I am at peace."

"My solar plexus is warm." Repeat five to six times.
"I am at peace."

"My forehead is cool." Repeat five to six times.
"I am at peace."

Progressive Relaxation

In 1929, Edmond Jacobson, a Chicago physician, published a book titled *Progressive Relaxation* in which he detailed the results of numerous case histories. His patients often responded favorably to his insistence that the relaxation state is incompatible with anxiety and tension. In his practice he found that by tightening selected muscle groups and then consciously letting the tension go, the patient could block stress-related symptoms. His technique has been widely and successfully used since that time.

Instructions
Practice Progressive Relaxation for two weeks for at least ten or fifteen minutes a day.

Get into a comfortable position.

Begin by bending your left hand back at the wrist (not at the elbow). While holding this position steadily for several seconds, notice the faint sensation in the upper portion of your left forearm. This sensation is the mark of muscle tension. It accompanies all effort and activity. Compare this sensation with the feeling in your relaxed right forearm. Become thoroughly acquainted with the sensation of tension so that you can recognize it whenever it occurs in any part of your body. Let your arm relax and notice how the sensation of tenseness diminishes when you let go completely.

Try bending your hand back several times, holding it for a few seconds, and then releasing it. Thoroughly explore the difference between the sensations of muscle tension and relaxation.

Progressive relaxation is a method of alternately tensing and relaxing each muscle group in your body. Progress from your toes to your legs to the muscles in your torso, your arms and hands, and end with your neck, facial muscles, and scalp.

Each time, gradually bring the tension up to high levels, hold it for several seconds, or until you experience some discomfort in the contracting muscles, and then release it gradually.

During your practice you will find that as you tighten your muscles you will gain a greater awareness of muscle tension, thereby allowing you to focus on it and control it. Also, your body contains built-in dampening mechanisms for any of its functions. Thus, as you forcibly contract a muscle an inhibitory nervous stimulus is sent to that muscle which tends to make the muscle relax more completely than would have been possible without the preceding contraction.

After each contraction, relax your whole body for ten to twenty seconds and feel the tension draining away.

If you practice Progressive Relaxation once a day you will find yourself becoming more and more effective in achieving a very relaxed state. Even when it is not possible to engage in total body relaxation, your increased awareness of the tension-relaxation sensations will allow you to perform differential relaxation, in which you carry out a task using only the necessary muscles while relaxing the rest of your body. This will save you a great energy expenditure and will promote a feeling of vitality and enthusiasm for whatever you are doing.

The following guideline has been included to provide a more structured practice session. It could be taped and replayed or someone could read it to you as you relax.

One by one, tighten each of your muscle groups, and then relax them on cue, saying to yourself, "Do it now" or "Now" for tensing, and "Relax" for releasing. The order of muscle groups should be:

> Left foot—left calf—left thigh—right foot—right calf—right thigh—stomach or abdominal muscles—chest muscles—shoulders—left hand—left forearm—left upper arm—right hand—right forearm—right upper arm—neck—mouth and jaw—eyes and nose—forehead—whole body at once

Hold the tension about five seconds or so. Focus all your attention on the feelings in those muscles. After releasing them, focus on the feelings of relaxation in those muscles for about fifteen seconds or so. Once you have relaxed a muscle group, let it go on relaxing while you focus on the next muscle group.

When you have finished all the muscle groups, review them in order to see if any tension still remains. If it does, let them relax more deeply. (Do not tense the muscles during this step.)

Remain still for a couple of minutes, noticing how relaxed your body feels.

Slowly count from five to one, beginning to gently move the parts of your body. You will feel refreshed, as if you have had a short nap.

Differential Relaxation

This is a way to relax while in an active state. It involves learning to differentiate between those tensions which are necessary to perform an action and those which are unnecessary. By becoming aware of undue muscle tension in everyday activities and reducing these muscular contractions, you can acquire a greater amount of energy which can be available for the actions you wish to perform.

As you do any daily activity, ask yourself whether the various tensions in your body are necessary. If they are not, consciously reduce them. After a period of time, this process will become automatic.

The Relaxation Response

Herbert Benson, M.D., of Harvard Medical School and director of the Hypertension Section of Boston's Beth Israel Hospital, has shown in clinical studies that the use of the Relaxation Response for ten to twenty minutes twice a day can be remarkably effective in improving total health and well-being. This system uses the muscle tensing and relaxing technique of Progressive Relaxation with the addition of a relaxation cue word which reflects your personal beliefs. There are eight steps to follow:

Step 1

Choose a personally important word or phrase to focus upon. It might simply be something like "peace," "calm," or "one," or a word that has special significance to your faith. It should be short enough to be said silently as you exhale normally.

Step 2

Choose a comfortable position.

Step 3

Close your eyes.

Step 4

Relax your muscles. You can use the Progressive Relaxation technique to tighten your muscles first or leave this part out and just simply relax each muscle group starting with your feet.

Step 5

Become aware of your breathing, and start using your focus word as you exhale.

Step 6

Maintain a passive attitude. Through regular practice, you will be able to disregard any thoughts that push their way into your consciousness.

Step 7
Continue for a set period of time. Keep a watch or clock in plain sight and look at it from time to time.

As you elicit the Relaxation Response by slowly going into it, so should you return to your everyday state in a slow, gradual manner. When you have finished, sit quietly for a minute or two to gently readjust.

Step 8
Practice twice a day. The method will be the most effective on an empty stomach, therefore it would be best to schedule your practice before breakfast and dinner.

Relaxing through Imagery and Visualization

By quietly enjoying restful mental images, your mind and body will experience a deep sense of peacefulness and a "letting go" that will bring about a state of deep relaxation.

This is a very simple way to counteract stress and tension. As you sit or lie in a comfortable position, begin to imagine a beautiful natural scene. It can be a favorite place that you have enjoyed or an imaginary one. Any number of your own images can serve as mental and physical relaxants. Just let your mind ride on the waves of your images. As your mind quiets, your body will also relax.

When your mind and body are deeply relaxed, your brain wave pattern actually changes and becomes slower. This deeper, slower level is commonly called *alpha level* (while your usual busy waking conscious level is called *beta level*).

To get to the alpha level easily, you might imagine a flight of stairs that are well lighted, carpeted, and perfectly safe to descend. See a handrail or anything that would help you to make a safe descent. Start at the top of the stairs and slowly visualize yourself walking down. Count the stairs as you descend. For example you might say: "Ten, down, nine, down, eight, deeper down, and so on," until you reach the bottom step. See yourself moving away from the stairs into a beautiful and peaceful natural setting. Stay in the alpha state for as long as you wish and then slowly come back up your staircase one step at a time.

Relaxing with Music
Using music to create a deep state of relaxation is extremely beneficial. Music allows you to move into another dimension where you are completely aware of the sounds that you hear. This state releases the stresses and tensions that you are carrying. The act of listening to soothing music allows your muscles to relax, your mind to become peaceful and all of the organs in your body to function more slowly, thereby giving a deep state of rest to your entire system. Since each person responds differently to music, it is important to select music that is peaceful and soothing to you. When you listen to music for the purpose of relaxation, you should set aside at least fifteen minutes of uninterrupted time.

When you have selected the music that you will use, you should allow your body to relax in a comfortable position with your eyes closed. If you focus your attention on the music, you will find that your cares and worries begin to drift away. You can mentally scan your body, noticing areas of tension begin to diminish and release as you start to become more deeply relaxed. Each time an unrelated thought comes into your mind, note it and discard it, remembering that your goal is to focus on the music. When the music ends, scan your body again and become aware of how relaxed you feel. As you practice your relaxation will be more and more complete.

If you would like to start a record or tape library of music for relaxation, the following suggestions may be helpful:

Title	Artist
The Golden Voyage (6 volumes)	Ron Dexter
Ancient Leaves	Michael Stearns
Spectrum Suite	Steven Halpern
Starborn Suite	
Zodiac Suite	
Eastern Peace	
Ancient Echoes	Steven Halpern and Georgia Kelly
Seapeace	Georgia Kelly
Tarashanti	
Birds of Paradise	
Autumn	George Winston
Healing Music	Joanna Brouk
To the Essence of a Candle	Larkin Stentz
Petals	Marcus Allen
	Jon Bernoff
	Teja Bell
	Dallas Smith
Silk Road	Kitarō

New Age and related music is available in New Age or metaphysical book stores all around the country.

Biofeedback

The clinical application of biofeedback was pioneered by Alyce and Elmer Green of the Menninger Foundation in the late 1960s. Biofeedback instruments are now accepted as being accurate, and are particularly useful because they tell you immediately where you are holding excess tension in your body.

Biofeedback works in the following way: You have two nervous systems. The voluntary or somatic system controls the nerve cells and fibers serving your skeletal muscles. These are the muscles employed in deliberate or consciously controlled movement, such as leg, arm or hand movement.

The second nervous system is called the involuntary or autonomic nervous system. This system regulates your heart, blood vessels, stomach, endocrine glands, and all of the physical functions which, before biofeedback, were thought to be outside of your voluntary control.

All physiological processes are accompanied by electrical activity. An impulse moving along a nerve, a contraction of a muscle, the operations of a gland, are all electrochemical events. Because they are electrical in nature, these processes can be detected by sensitive electronic devices.

In biofeedback, any internal change in either of these systems instantly triggers an external signal, such as a sound, a flickering light, or readings on a meter. When you are hooked up to the biofeedback equipment, you can see and hear the continuous monitoring of your selected body functions.

Biofeedback training allows you to take this information about your body states and use it to modify or change them.

Six measurements of physiological activity have been particularly useful in biofeedback: heart rate, blood flow and blood pressure, galvanic skin response, electrical activity of the brain and muscle tension.

Heart Rate
By recording the electrical activity of your heart and motion of the blood vessels, it is possible to accurately measure your heart rate. You can learn to lower that rate voluntarily using biofeedback equipment.

Blood Flow and Blood Pressure
When blood vessels constrict in times of stress, they not only cut off the rich supply of blood to your hands and feet, but they raise your blood pressure. As the capillaries constrict, they raise the peripheral resistance, which can be measured by an electrical device designed to indicate the amount of light passing through your fingers. The more blood passing through, the denser the filter and therefore, a smaller amount of light will be seen.

Galvanic Skin Response
The activity of your sweat glands changes the electrical properties of your skin. In times of stress the sweat glands are more active. The galvanic skin response can be measured easily by placing electrodes on your skin and feeding the information to a relatively simple biofeedback device.

Electrical Activity of the Brain
Individual nerves produce detectable electric currents when they are activated. The billions of nerve cells in your brain, therefore, can be measured by placing electrodes on your scalp and forehead.

Electrical Activity of Muscles
A major goal of all biofeedback techniques is the teaching of a motor skill designed to relax specific sets of muscles. The machine used to do this is called an electro-

myograph which gives a graphic representation of the electrical activity and tension of your muscles.

The rationale for using biofeedback training is that these machines promote a deep and well-defined level of relaxation that can be measured and charted. It is often less time-consuming than acquiring the same results by more traditional methods.

Sleep and Relaxation

The quality of your sleep is by far the most important indicator of your ability to relax. You will find that, as you practice one or more of the techniques in this chapter, your ability to fall asleep quickly and to sleep deeply and soundly each night will increase.

As you sleep your body is able to replenish and rebuild its energy supply. It is one of the few times when you can put your body on "automatic" and trust in its ability to heal and regenerate.

When you habitually go to bed late and arise early, you soon exhaust your body's regenerative capacity. Further, when you depend upon a loud noise to awaken you in the morning, you are stressing your adrenal glands and your autonomic nervous system through the "fight or flight" response. If this pattern is allowed to continue over a period of time, it can contribute to a chronic level of fatigue and lack of energy.

A good night's sleep is acquired when you consistently prepare early enough so that you can wake up naturally. Your body knows when it has had enough sleep and will awaken five or ten minutes before the alarm. This response can be programmed by going to bed earlier and earlier until you find yourself waking up naturally at the time you have selected.

It is also difficult to awaken filled with energy when you have had something heavy to eat the night before, especially if you eat or drink in the evening. When you adjust your eating, drinking, and retiring habits you will experience the rewards of renewed energy and vitality. This will become especially true as you continue to practice the relaxation techniques in this chapter.

The Eastern Concept

In the Eastern traditions it is felt that one's natural state is to live with both mind and body centered and relaxed. The Japanese word for repose of mind, soul or spirit is *anshin*, denoting a state of serenity and calmness which liberates vast resources of energy. This concept is exemplified in many Oriental art forms such as the following Zen poem, attributed to Chakun, a Zen scholar:

> The shadow of the bamboo sweeps the stair
> All night long
> Yet not a mote of dust is stirred.
> The moonbeams penetrate
> To the bottom of the pool,
> Yet in the water not a trace is left.

—Sokie-an, *Twenty-Five Koans*

To the Oriental mind, living in a state of calmness is the strongest state a person can achieve. In the modern world, in the East as well as in the West, it is continually possible to become overloaded with stimuli which cause the "fight or flight" pattern of response. As we have seen, high levels of stress and tension not only cause fatigue and illness, but can open the way to an enormous drain of your energy resources.

To counteract these tensions, it is common practice in Eastern societies to seek ways of enjoying a time of daily calmness and restfulness. For example, many Japanese homes focus inward through the use of indoor plants, small pools of water, and simple, harmonious surroundings. Just as the living space is turned inward and away from external distractions, it is also seen to be extremely useful to frequently experience exercises and meditations that bring about a state of internal stillness.

In the East, from ancient times, it has been thought that the mind and body are both born of the Ki of the Universe. The mind is seen as refined body, and the body unrefined mind. The mind is formless, colorless, odorless, and flies from place to place at will. The body has shape, color, odor, and its movements are restricted. To keep mind and body unified it is felt to be necessary to first focus the mind. In these cultures, the center of the Universe is said to reside in the Dantian and therefore, by concentrating this point, mind and body come together in a strong and powerful way.

Relaxation during Action

A principal idea in Eastern thought is the realization that when the mind is allowed to be agitated, the body will also respond in the same way. This is because the nervous system, passing along the spinal cord to the brain, controls the smooth functioning of the entire body. The brain can be considered the director and the nerves the messenger or information service. If the mind is calm these systems work in harmony. If the mind is upset, the nervous system reacts by sending messages which unbalance the body. Following is a quote from *Ki in Daily Life* by Koichi Tohei that perfectly expresses this idea:

> Just as the reflection of the moon shattered into thousands of splinters by the waves on the water fails to give a true impression of the moon, so if the spirit is turbulent it can give no true reflection of the universal. Turbulence can lead finally only to an inability to judge right from wrong and to a reversion to the rule of the instincts.
>
> We must unify our mind and body, calm the waves in the spirit, and make ourselves as a polished mirror in which the true reflection of the universal can clear our judgment and free us from mistaking good for bad.

All of the martial arts exemplify this concept. The participant learns to keep his muscles relaxed, refrain from worrying, and to flow with the action. Miyamoto Musashi, a famous seventeenth century Japanese *samurai*, exemplifies relaxation during action in *Go Rin no Sho* (The Book of Five Rings). The following is a quote from *The Water Book*.

> In strategy your spiritual bearing must not be any different from normal. Both in fighting and in everyday life, you should be determined though calm, meet the situation without tenseness yet not recklessly, your spirit settled yet unbiased.

His book often alludes to the fact that when you are tense and worried, you cannot see all of your options. When, however, you are able to remain calm and centered, you can flow smoothly and serenely through any difficulty.

Ki Breathing for Relaxation

The following Ki breathing techniques will send oxygen to every part of your body. They will also eliminate the waste products in your lungs as completely as possible. Slow, regular breathing gives more yin effects and produces the following results:

1. Your metabolism slows down and your body temperature tends to become slightly lower.
2. You experience a more tranquil and peaceful state of mind.

3. You relax all of the muscles in your body.
4. You produce a greater harmony among your body's systems and organs.
5. You send oxygen to every part of your body and use it as completely as possible.

Instructions

Lie on your back or sit in a chair that will allow your back to remain erect. Close your eyes.

Exercise 1

1. Breathe out for as long as you can.
2. Focus on the exhalation and the pause that comes after it.
3. Breathe in through your nose for as long as you can.
4. Focus on the inhalation and the pause that comes after it.
5. Allow your mind to concentrate on your breath and the Dantian at the same time. Send Ki to every part of your body as you inhale and send the impurities out of your body as you exhale. Continue this exercise for as long as you wish.

Exercise 2

1. With your lips slightly parted, exhale slowly making the sound "Ha."
2. Inhale slowly with your nose and silently form the sound "UUU" in the back of your throat.
3. After inhaling, focus your attention on the Dantian and retain your breath for a few seconds. Continue this exercise for as long as you wish.

Exercise 3

1. Hold a thin piece of paper in front of your face.
2. Inhale and exhale through your nose very slowly to the extent that the paper does not move.
3. The duration of the exhalation should be at least two times longer than the duration of the inhalation. Continue this exercise for as long as you wish.

The Poem of *Fang Sung Kung*

> With a high pillow I lie on my bed;
> I keep my body comfortable and relaxed.
> I breathe in and out naturally,
> And say the word *quiet* and *relax* silently.
> I think of the word *quiet* as I inhale,
> And the word *relax* as I exhale.
> As I silently say the word *relax*,
> I tell my muscles to relax.
> First, I relax my head, arms, and neck,
> Then my chest, abdomen, waist, and back.

Finally, I tell my legs and feet to become relaxed.
After repeating this three times to get my body at ease,
I tell all my organs and cavities to relax.
I keep my breathing rhythm steady, narrow and even
While focusing my attention on my abdomen.
As my mind enters into a state of mental quietness,
I enjoy this sleep-like but awake state of consciousness.
After I stay in this state for a short period of time,
I rub my face, get up, move around, and feel fine.

Rujing

In the practice of Qigong one of the most important goals is to experience *Rujing* which literally means to enter a state of quietness. Many attempts have been made in Chinese literature to define this state. The following are a few such descriptions:

"A process whereby one's mind is calm and at peace."
"A quiet and peaceful state of mind and body in harmony."
"A complete focus of mind on one thing."

When a person practicing Qigong is monitored in the state of Rujing with an EEG (electroencephalograph), alpha waves are seen to increase significantly. During Rujing the brain remains in a very calm state, just like that preceding sleep. This has been found to create conditions favorable for the regeneration of vitality throughout the whole body.

The following Rujing practices bring about a state of calmness and deep relaxation:

Exercise 1
1. Get into a comfortable position.
2. Focus on your breathing.
3. When you are ready, start to count the number of your breaths from one to ten. When you have reached ten start your count over again. Repeat the count for as long as you wish.

Exercise 2
1. Get into a comfortable position.
2. As you breathe slowly and easily, start to concentrate on one thing. It may be a person, a place, or anything that makes you feel content and happy. Continue your concentration for as long as you wish.

Exercise 3
1. Get into a comfortable position.
2. Concentrate on the Dantian and imagine a small ball or sphere located there.

Breathe deeply as you imagine this object fully. If it is comfortable for you to do so, imagine that it is filled with warmth or color or a slight pressure. Continue your concentration for as long as you wish.

Meditation

For centuries the Eastern cultures have used many meditation practices as a means of expanding and circulating Ki energy throughout the mind and body. In these traditions it is felt that the individual's consciousness is a single manifestation of a larger universal consciousness or energy which exists everywhere and in everything.

It is further believed that because the human mind is restless and seldom still, a veil is formed which brings about a sense of separateness and produces a sense of limitation. Through the process of meditation, however, which stills and calms the mind, inner boundaries slowly become dissolved bringing about a heightened state of identification with the universal consciousness. This, in turn, produces a feeling of profound contentment, relaxation, and fulfillment.

There have been many recent scientific studies in the Eastern and Western countries alike that have explored the effects of regular meditation practices. There is now an impressive body of documentation which indicates that when the meditator's mind and body transcend the limitations of moment-to-moment consciousness, a state of balance and centeredness is achieved. By decreasing the amount of internal and external stimuli one must respond to, the body's metabolism is lowered and alpha brain waves are greatly increased. Additionally, as cellular activity throughout the body slows, it reduces the need for oxygen while the increase in relaxation permits an increased flow of blood to the muscles which decreases the heart's workload. Finally, the cells of the brain fire in a synchronous manner, fostering integrated functioning between lower and higher brain centers and between left and right hemispheres.

The experience of meditation ultimately provides a profound sense of inner silence and tranquility, freeing the meditator from pressure, concern, tension, and anxiety. By decreasing these limiting states, additional energy becomes available to use in more positive ways.

There are three principles or inner activities involved in most forms of meditation.

1. Reflection and focused thought
2. Reception and quietness
3. Creation and formulation

Reflection and Focused Thought
There is already a strong element of meditation in everyone's life. When you focus your mind on a story you are reading, or when you are studying something that you wish to know, you are meditating or concentrating on one thing to the exclu-

sion of all other distractions. When you accomplish something through the power of concentration or focused thought you might not think of it as meditation and yet that is precisely what occurs.

Meditation also arises spontaneously when you focus your attention on a specific object or person such as a child at play, a beautiful place or a favorite painting.

Just as when your mind focuses outside it perceives the outer world, when you begin to look within, it discovers the beauty and tranquility of the inner world.

Reception and Quietness

The stillness and quietness experienced when in a state of meditation provides a deep rest for both your mind and body. Because your nervous system is allowed a period of recuperation, which can be even more beneficial than a restless night's sleep, you will notice an increase in your energy level each time you meditate.

When you meditate you also experience a heightened state of reception wherein the intuitive part of your mind is freed to make you more aware of your needs, give inspiration and even provide solutions to unresolved problems.

Creation and Formulation

By learning to focus uncritically on one thing at a time you develop a kind of self-discipline which increases your self-awareness. With practice, you can better understand and accept habitual patterns of perception, thought, and feeling which previously had an influence over your life without your complete awareness.

Through meditation you are able to go beyond your identification with the body and discover that you have an existence that is quite apart from your tensions and physical problems. You are also able to go beyond the mind by realizing that you are not your thoughts but the witness of those thoughts as they come and go.

You learn that your true identity is within the inner stillness, within the peace and satisfaction that is your own consciousness. When you have achieved that realization you can then use meditation to experience the powerful energies of imagination, visualization, and clear formulation of goals that ultimately bring about more positive and desirable life experiences.

Guidelines for Meditation Practice

Generally, meditation has been associated with religious doctrines and disciplines as a means of becoming one with God or the universe, finding enlightenment, achieving selflessness, and other virtues. It is, however, a well-documented fact that meditation can also be practiced independent of any religious or philosophical orientation, purely as a means of reducing inner discord and increasing self-knowledge.

The following guidelines will enable you to experience the benefits of meditation. If you remember that meditation, like sleep, does not need to be taught but comes naturally if you follow the right steps, you will progress rapidly and easily on your path.

1. Set aside a special place for meditation. It should be quiet and free of distractions. You should meditate in the same place each day if possible, because you create an atmosphere in your special place that will be conducive to your further practice.

2. Make sure that you are warm enough by choosing clothing that will be comfortable and also loose fitting.

3. Meditate at the same time each day. It is essential to begin to build a habit of meditation in your life. The morning and evening hours are good times to choose for your practice.

4. Instruct your mind to remain quiet for the duration of your meditation. If thoughts persist, just watch them come and go without involvement of any kind.

5. Plan your meditation with your eating needs in mind. Generally it is best to wait at least an hour after a meal. As meditation becomes a regular habit you will begin to prefer to eat lightly before or after your practice.

6. Regulate the flow of your breath when you begin your meditation. It is helpful to initially focus on your breath and to breathe slowly and easily. This practice also aids you in controlling the mind. As you meditate you should establish a slow, rhythmic breathing pattern which will allow your mind and body to relax in the meditation. It will soon seem as if the breathing continues on its own without your conscious awareness of a need for control.

Fig. 81

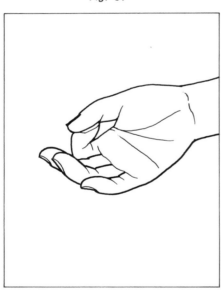

7. The traditional hand position is to rest your hands on your thighs with the tips of the thumb and index finger of each hand joined in the Yogic *chin mudra* (finger position). This aids your meditation by allowing the Ki energy in the meridians to flow freely to the fingertips and back up both your arms. If you find the *chin mudra* distracting in any way you can also meditate with your hands resting comfortably in an open position on your thighs.

8. The most commonly used meditation postures are the sitting or kneeling positions. It is helpful to sit or kneel on a pillow for added comfort and support. If sitting upright is uncomfortable for you, it is also possible to meditate lying down.

The posture you select should be maintained with your back, neck, and head in a straight line, preferably facing the earth's magnetic poles to the north or east. When you meditate you should feel steady and relaxed.

Fig. 82

A   B   C   D

Meditation Techniques

Because there are many different temperaments there are many different meditative techniques. If you have never meditated you might wish to try several of the following techniques to discover which one will be the best for you.

The main consideration in meditation is that it is a time to let go of your daily tensions and anxieties, a time to let your mind and body relax and just be. It is also a time to gain insights into your inner resources.

Witnessing

This is the purest form of meditation. It is simply sitting in meditation and watching the thoughts that come and go without judging or commenting. We are so caught up in our usual role of being absorbed with moment-to-moment thoughts that it is interesting to see what these thoughts consist of from a completely neutral position.

Vipassana

This is a Buddhist meditation that focuses on the rise and fall of the breath. *Vipassana* means "breath" and while the mind is engaged in this activity it cannot focus on its usual distractions. Your breathing should be gentle and regular. Just allow it to be the place where your mind is focused and enjoy the feeling of witnessing breathing rather than concentrating on it.

Zazen

Zazen means "just sitting." It is the basic meditation of Zen Buddhists for whom the path of enlightenment is everyday life lived with awareness and totality. Like all meditations, Zazen is a tool to help us rediscover the immediacy and freshness of ordinary life, as we did as children. The device used is to just sit and allow whatever happens to happen. Your mind will try to distract you with past and present concerns to take you away from fully experiencing the moment. Rather than focusing on these thoughts, the Zen Buddhists say that they are "paper tigers" and giving them attention only gives them more energy. Rather, the importance of this meditation is to just gain a feeling of sitting and experiencing the fact that you are not the mind and can ignore its chatter at will. If your mind is particularly rebellious, you can give it a distraction to play with such as concentrating on the Dantian or the breath.

The Kōan

In the Rinzai school of Zen, the master sets the disciple a *kōan* or riddle for his mind to focus upon. The riddle is impossible to solve, for example, "What is the sound of one hand clapping?" The Zen masters expect the disciple to remain in meditation until the mind gives up and remains silent. Having experienced *satori*, the state of "no mind" and the peace that accompanies this state, the meditator learns the difference between intellectual understanding and wordless experiencing with the body and senses. (This is not a meditation to attempt but is included here because the concept is fundamental to all meditation practices.)

Tratak (Gazing)

Another device to still the mind so that you can experience directly is "gazing." The object that you look at is not really important. Traditionally a lighted candle, a flower, a religious image or the picture of a guru can be used. The main point of the exercise is to keep your eyes on a central spot because not moving the eyes restricts the input of information for your brain to process. There is a limit to what views your mind will have concerning the image of a flower or a candle flame. When it tries to think about something else, keep bringing your attention back to the object of your contemplation. Your meditation is for the purpose of feeling the quality of the object, to relax, and enjoy what you are seeing.

Listening

Meditation is centered in the idea of relaxing and non-doing. You may hear but you cannot *listen* when you are thinking. As you center your awareness in music, chanting or natural sounds, you experience the essence of the sound, giving yourself the experience of emptiness, clarity, and receptivity.

Mantra

In this meditation the sound that is produced is internal. In the Sanskrit language, *man* is translated as "mind" and *tra* means "protection." The repetition of the *mantra* or sound evokes a deep and peaceful reaction throughout your body.

*Mantra*s are energies which are thought to have always existed in the universe. They pass in succession from teacher to disciple in an unbroken chain. The *mantra* leads the way to meditation and to a state of non-duality. Two typical Eastern *mantra*s are "Om" (I am) and "So-Ham" (I am he).

A *mantra* can be anything that you enjoy repeating. The words "flower" or "one" are often used as are names of saints or great teachers. For example, "Om Namah Shivaya" represents the God within. It should be repeated slowly, sounding each syllable: Om/Na/Mah/Shi/Va/Ya. Another, and perhaps the most widely used *mantra* in the world today is "Om Mani Padme Hum." In Sanskrit "Om" represents the universal energy or life-force, *Mani* means "jewel" or "crystal." *Padme* means "lotus," and *Hum* means "heart." Therefore the meaning usually ascribed to this *mantra* is:

> The entire universe is like a pure jewel or crystal within the heart of the lotus flower, which represents myself, and it is manifest in my own heart.
> —Dass, Ram, *The Only Dance There Is*

Choose a *mantra* that feels right to you. The *mantra* can be chanted out loud or repeated subvocally. *Mantras* are often used in conjunction with the breath to bring about a deeper meditation.

Meditation in Action

Everything can become a meditation, including the most ordinary everyday chores. What transforms daily activities into meditation action is awareness and whole-heartedness. The application of the Zen exhortation to give undivided attention to, and really feel the quality of each of your actions, is exemplified in the Japanese tea ceremony and the art of flower arranging. Being present in the moment imparts an unmistakable grace, effortlessness, and enjoyment to the "little things" that make up the greater whole of life.

The Microcosmic Orbit Meditation

The *Tao* means "the way" or "the power." In early Chinese writings the Tao implied an understanding of life which stressed individual harmony with the forces of nature. The Microcosmic Orbit is the foundation of the teaching of the Taoist system of meditation. Through their meditation experience and accumulated wisdom, the ancient Taoist masters learned the importance of the free circulation of Ki energy in the body. They discovered that they could learn to direct it to study this system and to gain a firsthand understanding of its benefits.

Bodywork

The Western Concept

For thousands of years some form of laying on of hands has been used to heal and restore the body's energy balance. The word *massage*, which is derived from the Greek *masso* (I knead) and the Arabic *mass* (to press softly), is used interchangeably for a number of systems that refer to body manipulation for realigning and reenergizing.

To the ancient Greek and Roman physicians, body manipulation techniques were one of the principal methods used for healing and relieving pain. In the early fifth century B.C. Hippocrates, the "father of medicine" wrote: "The physician must be experienced in many things, but assuredly in rubbing, for rubbing can bind a joint that is too loose, and loosen a joint that is too rigid." Julius Caesar's biographers have noted that he was daily "pinched all over" to ease his headaches and Pliny, the famous Roman naturalist, was in the habit of regular massage to relieve his congested breathing.

Over the years, various researchers have come to realize the significant role that touch has played in primitive societies. Many American Indian tribes use a light stroking method to balance and raise energy levels.

There are many body manipulation systems in existence, each having its own philosophy, techniques, health benefits, and limitations. The major distinction among bodywork systems is whether they are structure-based or energy-based.

Structure-based Systems
These systems arose from the Western traditions of science and medicine. They emphasize the correct alignment of muscles, bones, and connective tissue. They also view the human body as a structured machine and do not consider its subtle interactions to be of value in the healing process. Practitioners utilizing these methods prefer to work with body parts that can be seen and measured. Swedish massage, osteopathy, chiropractic, Rolfing, the Feldenkrais Technique and the Alexander Technique are examples of structure-based bodywork systems.

Energy-based Systems
These start from the assumption that all living matter possesses a life-giving force that circulates throughout the body and must be kept strong and free flowing to maintain health and energy. Most of the Eastern bodywork systems fall under this category.

Combined Systems
For the last seventy years there has been a growing interest in and acceptance of the Eastern philosophy of "vital force," or "life energy" within the Western health care systems. Many integrated systems have appeared since that time that combine

Eastern and Western medical and scientific concepts. These systems utilize methods for correcting structural problems and also for strengthening the body's energy systems as well. Foremost among these are Reichian therapy, polarity, and several forms of massage.

Structure-based Bodywork Systems

Osteopathy

The founder of osteopathy, Andrew Taylor Still, was a physician on the Union side in the American Civil War. He became disillusioned with the orthodox medical practices of the time and started treating his patients with his system for adjusting the spine. In his manual, *Osteopathic Technique*, Dr. Alan Stoddard states that: "Osteopathy is concerned with the establishment and maintenance of the normal structural integrity of joints, in order to restore them to their normal positions and mobility."

For the most part, an osteopath's work is focused on the spinal column. The spinal cord regulates the functioning of the autonomic nervous system and the spine also relates to the muscles and skeletal system. Therefore, keeping these two systems balanced and aligned is seen by osteopaths to be of prime importance in a patient's health care.

Chiropractic

Chiropractic is derived from a base similar to osteopathy. It was founded in 1895 by David D. Palmer of Iowa. He believed that a displacement in any part of the skeletal frame would also cause nerve dysfunction. Therefore, chiropractic is based on the idea that the spinal column is central to one's entire sense of well-being as it is instrumental in maintaining the health of the nervous system. Another vital chiropractic concept is that if the body is functioning in a balanced way, it has the capacity to cure its own illnesses and keep itself in perfect health.

Slight displacements of the spinal vertebrae, called *subluxations*, can be reflected in a wide range of symptoms. The aim of the chiropractor, therefore, is to find the subluxation and correct it manually.

Swedish Massage

This massage technique uses five classifications of manipulation. It was first developed by Henri Peter Ling at the turn of the nineteenth century and is rooted in the rigorous system of Swedish gymnastics. It imitates that system's vigorous methods for stimulating circulation. It can either stimulate or relax the body by the following methods:

1. Stroking (*Effleurage*)
This is the use of long, centripetal strokes that may be deep or superficial. It is used to increase blood flow.

2. Kneading (*Petrissage*)

Muscles are lifted from the bones, rolled, squeezed or wrung. This method stimulates the muscles and the deeper blood vessels as well as the lymphatic system.

3. Percussion (*Tapotement*)

Tapping, slapping, cupping or clapping the muscles brings about a stimulating effect.

4. *Friction*

Circular rolling movements around the joints is useful in breaking down adhesions. It also deeply stimulates the circulation.

5. *Vibration*

A rapid movement performed by the whole hand which has a stimulating effect upon the nervous system by acting on the nerve centers.

These techniques are most effective on the muscles, joints, nerves, and endocrine system. When used before an athletic workout, Swedish massage can prevent soreness and improve muscular performance. By stimulating the circulation of blood and lymph, it can speed the body's rehabilitation from injury.

Rolfing

In the 1940s Ida Rolf, whose formal training and doctorate was in biological chemistry, devised a system of manipulation using gravity as a tool for aligning the body. Her view of the human body was in terms of a child's tower of bricks. She wrote that if the body is correctly aligned everything functions smoothly. However if any part is out of alignment, as can happen as the result of an injury, an emotional trauma, or bad postural habits, then the structure become unstable.

Instead of the muscles performing their natural function of coming into action when, and only when, required, some of them must spend their whole time using energy to hold the structure in a standing position. Eventually they lose their elasticity, adhesions develop in the connective tissue which also can harden and energy is lost as the body adjusts to coping with supporting itself in a stressful way.

The Rolfing system, which she devised, uses manipulation that includes gravity as a tool for stretching and shifting the connective tissue back into a state of symmetry. Her system is also used to restore not only the structural integration of the body but the mental aspects as well. Rolf came to believe that by working to rebalance the physical body which holds certain postures due to emotions (tense with fear or bowed by grief), the therapist could elicit a release of emotional as well as physical stress and tension.

It was not until the mid-1960s that the ten session course, which is now the accepted practice, first became established.

The Alexander Technique

In the late 1800s Australian actor F. Matthias Alexander found that his voice was frequently strained. In setting about to discover the reason for this he found that it was due to the way he held his head when on the stage. His discovery led to other research that convinced him that, like Still and Palmer (the founders of osteopathy and chiropractic), the spinal column is the key to good health and ease of function.

He took their research one step further by teaching that if the vertebrae are out of alignment it is usually due to faulty postural habits. His premise was that by slumping and slouching we cause misalignments in our body that in turn drain energy and cause a corresponding mental habit pattern.

His method does not consist of a series of set exercises but rather a system for balancing and realigning according to individual need. He preferred to regard it as a system of reconditioning mind and body.

The Feldenkrais Technique

Feldenkrais, a Russian-born Israeli, began his career as an engineer and physicist. Having received his doctorate of science at the Sorbonne, he remained in France and began teaching his now famous method. His book *Awareness through Movement* states that, like the Alexander technique, one can improve posture through self-awareness. He believed that posture gives a first hand clue, not only of the physical stresses in a person's life, but of the mental conditioning as well.

His technique attempts to overcome the negative qualities of the unconscious movements that a person habitually uses. His treatment is designed to affect the personality structure by changing the physical structure.

Combined Bodywork Systems

Reichian Therapy

Wilhelm Reich combined a bodywork system in the 1940s with Freudian psycho-analysis. He used manipulation to dissolve the structural disorders in the body that he called "body armor" and which he considered to be physical manifestations of blocked emotional energy.

His deep tissue manipulation is done while the participant acts out deep emotional situations with the face, voice or body. The purpose of this is to trigger the memory and release of earlier emotional traumas.

Polarity Therapy

Polarity includes the Eastern theory that the body's energy fields must be balanced to maintain health and vitality. Health is seen as a delicate balance of physical, mental, and emotional energy.

Dr. Randolph Stone, the creator of the polarity system, began in the early 1900s to study many health fields throughout the world. He concluded that the human body consists of an intricate set of energy systems and that if there is a blockage of energy at any one point, the blockage can cause a malfunction throughout the entire body.

The term "polarity" comes from the fact that there are two sides, or poles, to everything in the universe. The polarity system uses a four part program to restore the body's two halves into a vibrant and harmonious whole.

Part One: Clear thinking
According to polarity theory, a positive mental attitude occurs when one accepts rather than rejects the intuitive, inner-knowing part of their nature.

Part Two: Bodywork
Using the chakra system of energy flow, this system teaches the application of gentle pressure to sensitive contact points to balance and tone the body's energy.

Part Three: Body movement
Known as polarity Yoga, this is a series of exercises and stretching postures that are easily integrated into a simple daily routine.

Part Four: Diet
Polarity therapy emphasizes the use of fresh fruits and vegetables and natural foods.

Reflexology
In the 1920s Dr. W. Fitzgerald postulated a theory that divided the body into "zones" of energy. This theory has since developed into what is now known as *Reflexology*. Many therapists using these methods are called "Zone Therapists."

For the reflexologist, there are ten energy channels that extend from the fingers and toes to the top of the head. Each channel represents a zone of the body and the corresponding organs located within that zone.

By feeling a client's hands and feet the therapist can detect which energy channels are blocked. By massaging them in ways which range from stroking to hard pressure, energy flow can be restored to its correct balance.

Although you would have to study with a trained reflexologist to understand this method fully, you can derive great benefit from massaging your hands and feet. We have included a suggested hand and foot massage for your interest in the self-massage section of this chapter.

182

Fig. 83

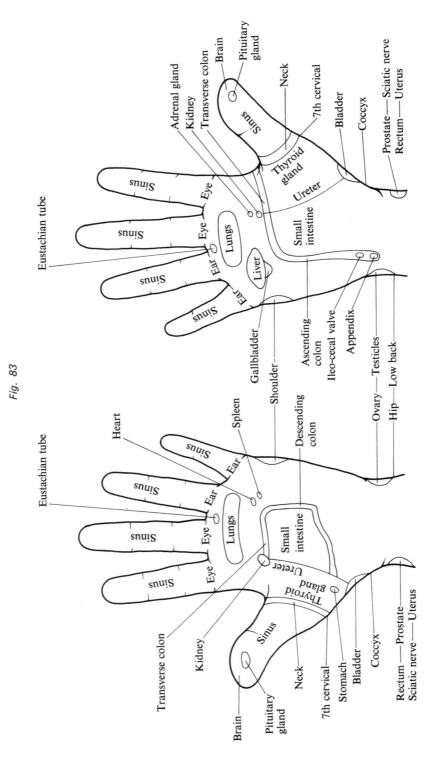

Right Hand (Palm up)

Left Hand (Palm up)

Fig. 84

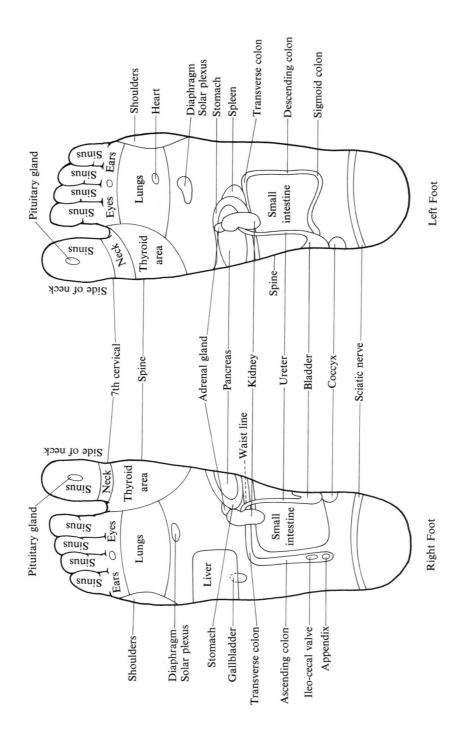

Left Foot

Right Foot

Massage

Massage was at one time considered to be an essential part of Western medicine. In the fifth century B.C., Hippocrates wrote long treatises concerning its effectiveness. Galen, another physician of ancient Greece, wrote a book on the subject. The Romans used it in conjunction with bathing, and for centuries it was thought to have energy raising and health giving properties.

Massage drifted out of fashion because the early Church viewed the techniques as sinful. After the last half of the sixteenth century, however, the writings of the French physician, Ambroise Pare, on the value of body manipulation to Western medicine, inspired other French physicians who began to use these methods in their practices. Based on this knowledge, Henri Peter Ling, a student at the University of Stockholm, Sweden, at the turn of the century, created the system known as Swedish massage. Massage was used extensively in the First World War to rehabilitate wounded soldiers. Later it again went out of fashion, as physiotherapists became attracted to other, more "modern" forms of treatment.

Recently, massage has been coming back into its own. There are many licensed therapists and with the continued growth and interest in "holistic health," massage has become a treatment of choice for many.

The Beneficial Effects of Massage

Massage has been effective in raising energy levels and reducing stress and tension. It improves the circulation in the muscles and tissues and stimulates circulation in the deeper blood vessels and lymphatic system. During massage toxic waste material is carried away from the cells and the immediate effects can be noticed in the rosy color of the skin.

Commonly Used Massage Methods

The methods of massage that are commonly used in the Western world today are the Swedish, the French, and the Finnish systems.

The Swedish system uses vigorous and bracing movements to exercise the muscles of a particular area or of the whole body.

The French system uses soothing and delicate manipulations of the face and neck. It is not as hard or as vigorous as the other methods.

The Finnish system is similar to the Swedish but use more brisk rubbing motions to increase circulation.

Finding a Massage Therapist

Most large cities have a number of state licensed massage schools where you can obtain a referral. You could call departments of physiotherapy at local hospitals or universities and you can also ask friends for a recommendation.

You should choose a therapist who has had several years experience and is licensed in your state (if it is a requirement of your state to be licensed in order to perform massage).

Self-massage

Although a complete massage must be performed by a licensed massage therapist, there are a number of self-massage techniques you can learn that will raise your energy level. These can be done anywhere and at any time that is convenient. Several of these techniques may be shared. When you take turns with a family member or a friend, you will find that massage is the basis for a special kind of communication and sharing. When you do self-massage you are also communicating with your body in a positive and healing way.

The Blackfoot Indian Massage

The Blackfoot Indians used this massage technique to raise energy levels and improve the flow of vital forces through the body. It can be experienced while wearing light clothing. The person receiving the massage should be lying on his or her stomach or seated in a comfortable position.

The person giving the massage stands or kneels on the left side, facing the head.

1. Place your index finger and middle finger together. Starting with the base of the skull and working down, draw your fingers down both sides of the spine. Use a firm, slow pressure.
2. Use your thumb on one side of the spine to work back up from the sacrum to the head. On that side only, press your thumb into the side of each vertebra and then flip it outward, as if you were digging out something from a small opening. Repeat on the other side of the spine.
3. Place your hands on the outer edges of your partner's shoulders. Gently massage both shoulders, working toward the neck. Massage up the neck to the base of the skull.
4. Finally, move both hands in a brisk sweeping motion down the neck and outward toward the shoulders. Continue this motion in widening circles down the spine.
5. Repeat this motion five or six times.

The following techniques can be experienced while wearing light clothing if you wish.

Commonly Used Massage Techniques

Soothing

This is a movement used to prepare the body for massage. It is a slow, circling movement which starts at the top of the shoulders. With the palms of both hands circle gently away from the spine and back to the center. The movement should be repeated several times.

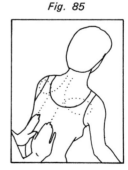

Fig. 85

Soothing

186

Fig. 86

Shoulder Kneading

Shoulder Kneading

Place your hands on the top of your partner's right shoulder, with your thumbs to the back of the shoulder, fingers to the front. Massage in a kneading motion to the count of ten. Repeat to the left side. Repeat to each side several times.

Hand Sliding

Place your right hand, little finger side down, on the top outer edge of your partner's right shoulder. Apply slight pressure against the surface of the shoulder with the edge of your hand. Using a continuous vibrating motion, move your hand sideways toward the base of the skull. Repeat to each side several times.

Fig. 87

Hand Sliding

The following massage techniques are excellent for raising energy levels:

Tapotement

Variation 1: Place both hands, little finger side down, on your partner's right shoulder. With a light chopping motion alternate your right and left hand as you gently move toward the base of the skull. Repeat three times to each side.

Variation 2: Place your hands in a cupped position on your partner's upper back. Tap using alternate hands for five seconds.

Variation 3: Place the backs of your hands on your partner's upper back. Alternate your hands rapidly to perform this technique. Repeat for five seconds.

Fig. 88

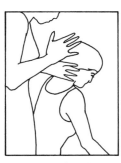 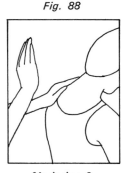 

Variation 1   Variation 2   Variation 3

Basic Self-massage Routine

The following routine takes ten or fifteen minutes and will raise your energy level each time you practice it. It is best to wait at least one hour after a meal or longer if it has been a heavy one.

Repeat each of the following exercises for as long as you wish.

1. Scalp Tapping
Apply friction to your scalp using your fingertips. Rub and tap your head with a gentle motion until you feel a tingling sensation in your scalp.

2. Eye Palming
Place your hands over your eyes. Cross your fingers but do not press on your eyes. Close your eyes and relax for as long as you wish.

3. Face Massage
Rub your hands vigorously together to warm them. Place them on your face with your fingers over your eyes. Do this several times. Rub your hands together again and smooth your forehead, cheeks, and chin. Rub out your frown lines.

Lightly tap the entire surface of your face.

Place your index and middle fingers on each jaw. Open and close your mouth to release tension in your jaw.

4. Neck Squeezing
Interlock your fingers behind your neck and squeeze with your palms. Repeat several times.

5. Arm Massage
With your right hand rub the whole length of your left arm from the back of your left hand to your left shoulder. Stroke down the inside of your left arm to your wrist. Repeat several times. Change and repeat with your left hand.

6. Chest and Stomach Massage
Rub your hands vigorously together. Use your right hand to gently smooth and massage your chest, upper and lower abdomen. Use a rhythmic clockwise motion. Continue as long as you wish.

7. Leg Massage
Both legs may be massaged using the left hand for the left leg and the right hand for the right leg. Stroke down from your hips to your ankles. Massage your ankles. Change to the inside and massage the inside of your legs working back up to the upper inside thighs.

8. Back Massage
Rub your hands vigorously together. Squeeze and knead your left shoulder muscle with your right hand. Do the same with your right hand squeezing your left shoulder. Make a fist with each hand and *gently* tap your back as far as you can reach. Focus on your lower back.

9. *Hand Massage*

Rub your hands vigorously together. Pull each finger from the base to the tip, using your thumb and index fingers of the opposite hand. Firmly massage the base of each finger and the web between your fingers. Massage the palm of your hand and the back of your hand with a gentle but firm circular motion. Massage your wrist. Continue for as long as you wish.

10. *Foot Massage*

Rub your hands vigorously together. Massage the sole of each foot in turn. Massage your toes and the web between your toes. Pull and rotate your toes. Rub your instep and each ankle. Smooth each side of your Achilles tendon in a downward movement. Repeat several times with each foot.

11. *Relax*

Allow a few minutes after your massage to just relax and enjoy the warm, tingling sensations in your body.

The Eastern Concept

The origins of Eastern medicine can be traced to Huang-di, known as the Yellow Emperor (2764 B.C.). To Huang Ti is attributed the first great Chinese medical classic, *Huang-di Nei Jing, The Yellow Emperor's Classic of Internal Medicine,* a book which was compiled sometime between 500 and 300 B.C. This work consists of a dialogue between the Yellow Emperor and his chief minister, Qi Bo, on the subject of wellness. It is here, for the first time, that the theories of yin and yang, the Tao and the Five phases of Ki are outlined along with many other healing methods which have been constantly in use throughout the centuries. These methods include many kinds of bodywork which raise Ki by restoring the body's energy balance.

Most of the bodywork systems currently in use are based in the ancient systems of massage and acupuncture/acupressure. For our purposes we will concentrate on these two time-honored methods.

Acupuncture

In Oriental medical theory, Ki energy in the body is said to run along a series of channels or "meridians." These correspond to, but are independent of, the nerve and blood vessel networks and have branches of their channels located in the superficial portion of the skin.

There are twelve main meridians in the body, one of which corresponds to each of the major organs: the lungs, heart, stomach, spleen-pancreas, large intestine, small intestine, liver, gallbladder, bladder, and kidney; plus the pericardium (the membrane which surrounds the heart) which corresponds to the blood vessel system, and the "triple warmer." The triple warmer does not have a direct equivalent in Western medicine. It is regarded as the link between the three parts of the body (upper, middle, and lower) and it also regulates the flow of fluids and temperature in the body.

Each of the meridians have specific starting and ending points, a sequence and direction of energy flow, and internal connections with their related organs as well as with other meridians. Meridians are bilateral, running on both sides of the body, and each has low electrically resistant points along its course (*tsubo*) which can directly affect the energy flow in the meridian, related organ or a specific part of the body. There are over three hundred such points. New points are added as their value is discovered.

The term "acupuncture" derives from the Latin word *acus* (needle) and puncture (to prick). It is used to describe a technique in which needles are used to puncture the skin at certain defined points in order to restore the balance of Ki energy.

There is an interesting story that suggests that acupuncture was discovered in China thousands of years ago by mistake; it was noted that soldiers who were wounded with arrows often recovered from diseases that had plagued them for years. Imitating the effects of the arrow, Chinese doctors began to puncture the skin with needles at certain points in an effort to determine the relationship between various body parts and the organs affected.

At first, the acupuncture needles were made of stone quarried from rich jade deposits in the mountains of China, later bone or bamboo was used. When metal was discovered, the needles were made of iron, silver, copper, gold, and other alloys; today's needles are made of processed stainless steel, gold, and silver.

In the Orient today acupuncture is often used as a general anesthesia during surgery. Patients report no pain during surgical procedures and, more importantly, no aftereffects. There are currently more than a million Eastern doctors who use some form of acupuncture in their daily practice.

Skilled acupuncturists often make their diagnosis by feeling the pulse points which represent a patient's meridians. Quietness, overactivity, underactivity, hardness or fullness of the pulse points can indicate an excess or depletion of the energy flow through the meridian. When malfunction occurs in a certain organ, points along the corresponding meridian can be sensitive when touched.

During treatment the acupuncture needles are inserted and manipulated according to the acupuncturist's diagnosis. The needles can stimulate more energy flow or relax the meridian to decrease and balance the energy. The major sensations reported by patients, who use this method, include a feeling of lightness, of increased energy and a corresponding lift in mood and well-being.

There are a number of reasons why acupuncture works. First, it simply stimulates the body's own regenerative powers, the same powers that cause us to flush the eye with tears when a piece of dust is lodged under the eyelid or to cough forcefully when a small piece of food enters the windpipe. Secondly, it increases circulation, which is always beneficial to health.

Recent research results indicate still another important reason. The insertion of acupuncture needles stimulates the nerves and causes the brain to release endorphins, painkillers manufactured in the brain that work like morphine.

There is an Eastern explanation of how and why this ancient system works. In these societies Ki is seen as the life-force that is in a constant state of fluctuation.

> True Ki is the original Ki. Ki from Heaven is received through the nose and controlled by the windpipe; Ki from food and water enters the stomach and is controlled by the gullet. That which nourishes the unborn is the Ki of former heaven (prenatal); that which fills the born is called the Ki of the latter heaven (postnatal).
>
> *The Yellow Emperor's Classic of Internal Medicine*

In the Western tradition, lack of air, food or water would be considered sufficient cause for depletion and illness. In the Eastern cultures this obvious condition would not be ignored nor denied but would also not be considered a complete fact.

Closer to their way of thinking would be the inclusion of the idea that the vital energy of life must be supplied by air, food, and water. Therefore, it is the vital energy that can be depleted and can also be restored through the use of acupuncture.

Acupuncture and Yin and Yang

In the Oriental cultures the law operating throughout all existence states that yin and yang are opposites and must succeed one another. As it applies to acupuncture, the body is divided into yin and yang regions.

Yang	*Yin*
Body surfaces	Interior of the body
Spine and back	Chest and abdomen
Male	Female
Clear body fluid	Cloudy body fluid
Ki energy	Blood
Protecting	Nourishing

The twelve basic meridians are similarly divided into the yang (hollow) organs and the yin (solid) organs.

Yang	*Yin*
Gallbladder	Liver
Small intestine	Heart
Stomach	Spleen-pancreas
Large intestine	Lung
Bladder	Kidney
Triple warmer	Pericardium

The yang organs are simple pipes which transport food, transmute it into nutrients for the body use, and eliminate waste products which result from the process. The yin organs are much more complex. They produce and store Ki which nourishes the body. An acupuncture treatment strives to balance the Ki between the yin and yang aspects of each pair.

The qualities of yin and yang are consistent throughout the entire structure of the body as seen from this point of view. For example, the surface of the body is yang, the interior is yin. The surface of every internal organ is always yang and its interior always yin. This description carries down to the individual cells which are also thought to be yang on the outside and yin on the inside.

Acupuncture is also seen to provide a balance of yin and yang, insuring that there is never an excess of either.

Acupuncture and the Five Elements

As we have already seen, the Eastern traditions divide the elements of the world into five categories. These categories are relevant to the acupuncture meridians and their related organs because it is felt that each human being is a microcosm of the universal principle. The meridians relate to the Five Elements in the following manner:

Fig. 89

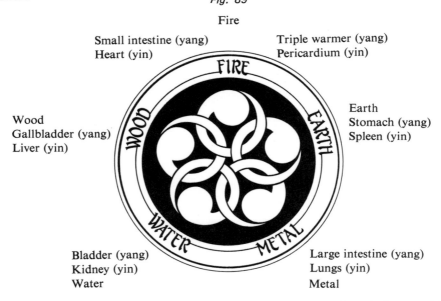

Fire

Small intestine (yang)
Heart (yin)

Triple warmer (yang)
Pericardium (yin)

Wood
Gallbladder (yang)
Liver (yin)

Earth
Stomach (yang)
Spleen (yin)

Bladder (yang)
Kidney (yin)
Water

Large intestine (yang)
Lungs (yin)
Metal

For abundant health and energy there must be a harmonious balance of Ki energy between each of the Five Elements just as a balance must be maintained between the yin and yang pairs of meridians.

We can understand the interplay of the Five Elements as we relate them to the interaction of their energies in nature. Wood provides the energy that produces Fire. Fire forms ashes which decay to produce Earth. Earth energy forms and gives birth to Metal. Metal is harder to relate to, but when heated Metal becomes liquid (Water). Water is the nourishment for the production of Wood.

Each meridian's energy has this same type of interplay and depends on the condition of all of the others to maintain health.

In an acupuncture treatment, a problem is solved by looking at the imbalance of Ki within a particular meridian, relating it to the energy of the Five Elements and all the other meridians, and then balancing the energy accordingly.

Finding an Acupuncturist

The American Medical Association still regards acupuncture as an experimental medical procedure. Some insurance companies will pay for acupuncture performed by a licensed acupuncturist if the procedure is legal in the state where it was performed (California, Hawaii, Nevada, and New York), and if the procedure was prescribed by a physician; many other insurance companies will pay for acupuncture if it is performed by a physician.

The best way to find a qualified acupuncturist is to look in your local telephone listings for acupuncture clinics or doctors of Oriental medicine. You could also ask for a referral from your physician.

Acupressure

With acupressure you can obtain many of the same benefits that can be derived from acupuncture. You can do self-acupressure or find a professional acupressurist, many of whom are listed in your local telephone book.

There are points found on each meridian that bring the body into balance by stimulating, sedating, or balancing the energy flow. These points are easily found and lend themselves well to fingertip stimulation because of their pressure responsive nature.

The purpose of stimulating a meridian is to bring a fresh supply of energy to that particular meridian which is low or deficient in energy. When energy is lacking in a meridian, the organ involved, as well as its corresponding muscles and nerves, is working at a deficient level. This can ultimately have an adverse effect upon the vitality of your entire body. Stimulating the specific point has a revitalizing effect on that particular energy flow and therefore, it helps to remove blocks or dams in the organ's system which could have prevented a state of good health.

We instinctively know which places on our body to rub when we are experiencing discomfort because the body has its own system for safeguarding its health. When your eyes feel tired, you rub them. We wring our hands when we feel anxious and if we have a headache, we frequently rub our temples or the sides of our head. In so doing we contact many of the pressure points that bring relief. Whenever we are hurt, we involuntarily massage the pain away just as when a child falls, he instinctively rubs the area that causes pain.

There are several forms of acupressure that are being practiced today. They all use finger pressure to balance, stimulate, and release energy from the specific points along the meridian pathways but the method of approach is different for each one. The main types of acupressure include:

Shiatsu: Shiatsu uses a series of points which are pressed for a few seconds in a vigorous fashion. The points run consecutively along an energy flow and the pressure should be firm. It is usually done by a therapist who combines acupressure with massage.

Dō-In: Dō-In acupressure is self-acupressure. It includes a set of stretching exercises as well as self-massage at specific points. It also includes a set of breathing exercises and incorporates these with the exercises to form a daily program of practice.

G-Jo: G-Jo, or acupressure for first aid, utilizes specific points in response to symptomatic needs. In this type of acupressure it is necessary to be aware of the specific points that act to relieve the discomfort, injury or disease of each part of the body.

Jin Shin: Jin Shin acupressure uses prolonged finger pressure. It focuses on the balancing of the meridians and correct functioning of the organs. It uses the pressure of two points at one time which stimulates the flow of energy between the two points. It can be self-administered or done by a therapist.

All of these forms of acupressure can be perfectly blended with other disciplines

194

such as Yoga or massage because they also focus on balancing and energizing the body.

Using Acupressure Points to Balance the Ki
Each of the twelve main meridians has a balancing point which is located on the meridian that it controls. The function of a balancing point is to evenly distribute that meridian's Ki. It also provides Ki to the organ specifically related to the meridian. Therefore, this point automatically reestablishes the meridian's energy balance whether the meridian energy is excessive (blocked) or deficient (lacking or low).

Suggestions for Working with Acupressure Points
1. Sit in a comfortable position.
2. Press the points for two minutes.
3. Press the same point on each side of your body.
4. Use your finger or thumb.
5. Pressure should not be extreme; a steady, light pressure is all you need.
6. If you wish, you may gently rotate your pressure finger as you hold the point.
7. Practice as often as you wish.

The following diagram will help you to locate the Balancing Point for each meridian.

Fig. 90   Balancing Points

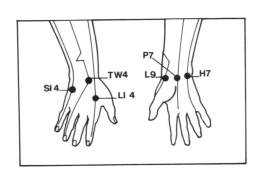

Meridian	Point
Lung	Lung 9
Large intestine	Large intestine 4
Stomach	Stomach 42
Spleen	Spleen 3
Heart	Heart 7
Small intestine	Small intestine 4
Bladder	Bladder 64
Kidney	Kidney 3
Pericardium	Pericardium 7
Triple warmer	Triple warmer 4
Gallbladder	Gallbladder 40
Liver	Liver 3

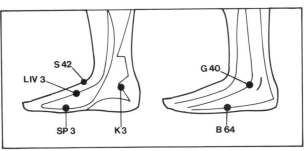

Inside   Outside

Using Acupressure Points for Relief of Symptoms
Acupressure points can be used for the relief of symptoms of problems by selecting points which are connected to the meridian relating to the problem. You may also select points that are in the general area of the problem. If your problem is complex, you should seek out an acupressurist who has a greater understanding of the interrelationships of the Ki in the various meridians as they relate to your symptoms.

The following suggestions have been included so that you can try the use of acupressure for yourself.

For headaches—Large intestine 4
Looking at the back of your hand, locate the point at the base of the web between the thumb and index finger.

For shoulder tension—Triple warmer 10
At the outside end of the crease of the elbow, against the bone. Bend your elbow and follow the crease toward your elbow.

Fig. 91

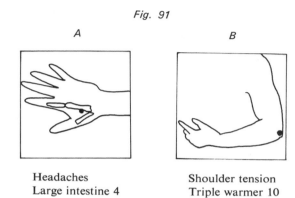

A   B

Headaches
Large intestine 4

Shoulder tension
Triple warmer 10

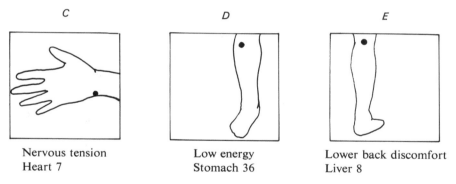

C   D   E

Nervous tension
Heart 7

Low energy
Stomach 36

Lower back discomfort
Liver 8

For nervous tension—Heart 7
With the palm of your hand facing you, look at the crease at your wrist. This point is on the little finger side of the major crease of your wrist.

For low energy—Stomach 36
As you bend your knee, place your fingers along the bottom edge of the kneecap. This point is about 1 inch below the placement of your little finger and on the outside edge of the shinbone.

For lower back discomfort—Liver 8
At the center of the crease behind the knee.

When using these or other acupressure points it is important to press or massage an area that is very specific in location because the pressure points are quite small (approximately three-eights of an inch in diameter). It is also important to use a firm pressure, however it should not be so strong that it is painful. Pressure should be maintained for about two or three minutes. During that time you may feel the release of tense muscles under your fingers. This will allow you to apply slightly more pressure. You may also feel a sudden pulse under your fingers. This is an indication of the flow of Ki becoming established in the acupressure point. Do not press on areas of the body where there are evident injuries or inflammation.

If you would like to learn more about acupressure there are several resources available in most large cities. Many acupuncture schools also teach acupressure classes. There are usually acupressure teachers associated with doctors of Oriental medicine. Also, colleges and universities are beginning to offer acupressure courses in their extension programs.

Shiatsu

Although they may differ in method, both Western and Eastern massage derive from the instinctive use of the hands in healing. Competent shiatsu practitioners are able to feel the Ki in their patient's bodies and utilize the necessary amount of finger pressure to draw, realign, and disperse this energy. The Japanese word for this kind of treatment is *teate*, and for conditions that are more acute, *te-okure*. Both include the word for hand, which is *te*, and suggest the importance of the use of hands in raising energy and healing.

Shiatsu, which originated in Japan, has been recognized worldwide for over seventy years. The word means "finger," *shi*, and "pressure," *atsu*.

The shiatsu system is based on Chinese medical theories that were introduced to Japan about a thousand years ago. At that time, *amma*, a form of massage, was well-known and used by Japanese physicians. When the Japanese government issued regulations requiring that *amma* practitioners be licensed, many began to integrate other techniques such as Dō-In. *Amma* became used more for pleasure and shiatsu, now the more formal system of bodywork, became used for treatment and healing, often borrowing from Western medical theory to explain its results.

Like acupuncture and acupressure, shiatsu is based on promoting health by stimulating Ki energy, using pressure on the skin at various points along the meridians.

The system of shiatsu was codified and first taught by Tokujirō Namikoshi. It is calming and relaxing, using the acupressure points, but differs from acupressure by employing certain body manipulations and movements as well.

Pressure is applied in a great variety of ways. Sometimes the fingers are used, sometimes the thumb, the palm or heel of the hand, or a knee, an elbow or the soles of the feet. There is no set order to a shiatsu treatment, each therapist devises his or her own routine according to your needs.

To a limited extent it is possible for the lay person to learn how to apply these techniques. However, it is important to find a reputable shiatsu therapist for any extensive work.

There are also special shiatsu exercises that can be used to raise your energy levels.

Shiatsu Exercises

Most shiatsu practitioners advise simple exercises, which are effective for raising your energy levels. These exercises, which concentrate on stretching, rotating, and moving muscles and limbs, can be practiced often. They keep the Ki energy balanced and flowing throughout your body. Unlike most Western exercises, which tend to make the body hard and muscular, shiatsu exercises help to make it soft and flexible. This is similar to Yogic exercises and Aikidō.

Fig. 92

Exercise 1

Sit on your heels and press your fingers firmly under your rib cage. Take a deep breath, then, as you breathe out, bend forward as far as you can. Press your fingers firmly into your solar plexus. This releases abdominal Ki.

Exercise 2

Tension is frequently held in your neck and shoulders. This exercise will ease a stiff neck and release the blocked Ki energy.

Sit with your legs wide apart. If possible, keep your knees on the floor. Clasp your hands with the palms turned up. Take a deep breath and pull up. Straighten your back as much as you can. Without twisting, bend sideways as far as possible as you exhale. Take another breath as you sit up and repeat to the other side.

Fig. 93

Fig. 94

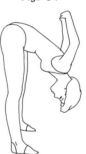

Exercise 3

To relax your shoulders and back: stand with your feet slightly apart. Clasp your hands behind your back. Inhale. As you exhale slowly, bend forward, raising your arms behind your head as far as you can. Slowly straighten up and inhale. Repeat several times.

EXTENDING KI

The Western Concept

As you learn to raise your Ki energy by interacting with the materials presented in the preceding chapters, you will increasingly enjoy a sense of extending more energy into everything that you do.

We would like to share with you an important additional concept that will aid you to extend your Ki energy fully and will also help you to derive the most benefit from your "Ki raising" practices. That is the concept of focusing your mind in positive and constructive ways.

As we have seen in Chapter 5, the mind moves the body and therefore one single thought can create tremendous power. That is why changing negative thoughts and behavior patterns into positive ones can become most important when seen from the point of view of extending Ki.

Smiling, Laughing, and the Positive Emotions
Good spirits are a vital part of life. According to Norman Cousins, adjunct professor of Biobehavioral Studies at the University of California, Los Angeles, focusing on the positive emotions can bring about a state of health and well-being. As his own case history abundantly illustrates, the emotions of hope, faith, love, will to live, creativity, laughter, determination, and purpose create corresponding physiological changes. In his book, *Anatomy of an Illness*, Mr. Cousins recounts how his decision to focus on these emotions brought him through a life threatening illness. He has since shared his knowledge with many others for whom a conscious willingness to explore the revitalizing emotions has brought about numerous benefits.

When you concentrate on the positive emotions you smile and laugh more often and accept those around you in a happy and nonjudgmental way. Just the simple act of smiling is an instant way for two people to communicate. There are no language barriers when you are smiling.

On a deeper level, when you are smiling, you are also triggering happier memories within you body. According to a study from Clark University, it does not matter whether you are smiling sincerely or faking it, your body's response will be the same. Dr. John Diamond, author of *Your Body Doesn't Lie*, suggests that smiling increases the flow of thymus secretions necessary for a balanced immune system. Moreover, he notes that just viewing a smiling face gives you more life energy.

Besides allowing you to ease stored physical tensions and rigidity, there are many physiological changes that occur when you experience a hearty laugh. The deep breathing and full exhalations thoroughly ventilate your lungs and send surges of vitality throughout your body. Norman Cousins calls it a form of "inner jogging." Besides stimulating respiration, laughter also stimulates your blood circulation sending an extra supply to your head and face. Your glands secrete hormones called *catecholamines* that act as regulatory agents in your system and your pituitary gland stimulates the release of endorphins which are natural painkillers that make you feel energized and alert.

In addition to providing physiological benefits, laughter and the positive emotions are of great psychological value, helping to release fear and anxiety. According to Dr. Harvey Mindess of Antioch University in California, when we are in touch with the playful part of ourselves, there is a quality of fulfillment, peacefulness, and energy that emerges. We feel good about ourselves when we take time for playfulness and recreation. We then are able to share our spontaneity with others as we become more open to communicating and sharing.

Each time you become totally engrossed in something "just for the fun of it," all restrictions and limitations disappear from your consciousness and you become centered and focused in the present, in the here and now. In this way you experience the present moment completely. Through enjoyment and a sense of playfulness your energy is ignited rather than spent, which allows you to simply relax and absorb the life energies that surround you.

The Eastern Concept

In the Eastern cultures universal energy is considered to be available for whatever uses you wish to make of it. From this point of view you are either "extending Ki" or "pulling Ki." By choosing to extend Ki you become centered in the universal Ki which promotes a vigorous and positive life. Pulling Ki, conversely, is seen as a negative condition which ultimately leads to a loss of vigor and well-being. It is, therefore, of importance for each individual to consciously decide which attitude should prevail in his or her daily life.

According to the theory of yin and yang, the way to dissipate darkness is with light; the way to overcome cold is with heat; and the way to overcome negative thoughts is to substitute positive thoughts in their stead as exemplified by an ancient Japanese proverb which says: "Happiness comes in through a laughing gate."

Emotions are a very important part of our daily life and in many Eastern healing systems, from acupuncture to massage, they are viewed as intimately connected to the physiological functioning of the internal organs. The liver is thought to dominate anger while the heart dominates joy. The spleen corresponds to thinking and worry and it is felt that excessive negativity will ultimately damage spleen functions thereby impairing the immune system. The lungs dominate grief while the kidneys control fear.

The emotions are also seen to control the state of your Ki energy. Joy and positive emotions cause Ki to slow down and flow smoothly. However, the negative emotions have the ability to cause an imbalance in your mind and body if allowed to predominate in your life. For example, it is thought that anger causes Ki to go upward; worry causes it to stagnate; grief causes Ki to disperse; fright causes it to scatter; and fear causes it to descend.

In the Eastern traditions it is felt that the best way to overcome these imbalances is by learning and practicing specific methods for calming the mind. In this way a state of harmony and balance can be achieved on a lasting basis.

Strengthening Ki by Calming the Mind

Your brain continually gives off electromagnetic vibrations called *brain waves*. When you are upset for any reason the waves become uneven and create even further agitation. By learning to unify the mind, the mind and body both enter a state of unity as exemplified by a meditator during a state of deep meditation.

One of the most valuable and practical methods for strengthening Ki energy by calming the mind is provided by master Kōichi Tōhei and his disciples. They have recently published several works that explain clearly how and why this concept is essential to your health and vitality. The following is a brief description of Master Tōhei's philosophy:

The Four Basic Principles to Unify Mind and Body

1. *Calm and focus the mind at the "one point" in the lower abdomen.*

   Ki energy as it expands and contracts is continually in motion. The disciplines of Oriental health and fitness techniques, medicine, and the martial arts all have in common a method for harnessing and controlling that powerful energy. In each of these disciplines the Hara or Dantian, located approximately three inches below the navel, is seen to act as a powerful transformer radiating Ki outward and absorbing it from all directions. By focusing attention on the "one point" when working with these disciplines, one can begin to use the centeredness and stability that result to reach the desired goal.

   The Dantian takes its name from the pattern made as several meridians cross at the abdomen, making lines resembling the Chinese character 田 (den). One of the reasons that the Dantian is used as a center of focus is because it is here that many autonomic nerves are gathered. By centering attention at this point, the nerves and accompanying blood vessels become regulated which, in turn, helps to regulate the body's basal metabolism.

   The Oriental traditions share the belief that a mind without a strong center of focus is easily moved in every direction. Because the body is thought to follow the mind, strength and vitality can suffer if the mind is not brought under control. They further believe that by placing attention on the "one point," the mind automatically concentrates on the sixth chakra or "third-eye" (called *Tentei*, in Japanese). Many of the breathing techniques given in Chapter 3, the exercises in Chapter 4, and the relaxation exercises in Chapter 5 include the concept of focusing on the "one point."

2. *Release all stress from the body.*

   As you have seen in Chapter 5, true relaxation is much more than a pleasant or collapsed state. It is important to further understand that real strength is only inherent in the kind of relaxation that removes all negativity from your mind and body. Conversely, loss of power resides in states that mimic relaxation but are only allowing you to mask or hide stored anger or tension. By focusing your attention on the "one point" and relaxing completely, your strength is centered, balanced, and secure.

   In Mr. Tōhei's book, *Ki in Daily Life*, he tells the story of the "magic pot" by way of illustration of this principle. It is about a merchant who had an expensive pot for sale. When the people would not buy it because of the expense he told them that it was a "magic pot" and that they could prove its worth by throwing whatever they disliked into the pot. When they did, the pot caused everything to disappear completely.

   Mr. Tōhei's thesis is that we all have such a magic pot in the "one point" in the lower abdomen. It can engulf everything. Therefore, by throwing all tensions and negative emotions into the Dantian, one can maintain a perpetually relaxed state of mind and body. By this means it becomes possible to develop a strong sense of Ki as you act according to an old Zen proverb which states: "Think something which cannot be thought." Mr. Tōhei tells us that if you practice reducing the "one point" to a size too small to imagine, your mind will become infinitely calm, as you become naturally immovable by becoming one with the universe in this way.

3. *Keep the weight of every part of the body at its lowest point.*
Because of the law of gravity the weight of any object naturally falls to its underside, the side closest to the center of the earth. The human body also responds to the same principle.

When you are holding excess tension in your body you are out of balance and harmony with the universal Ki. Your weight is then held in the upper part of your body, requiring a tremendous energy expenditure just to maintain an upright position. This continually exhausts your energy supply and makes it difficult to move or act spontaneously and gracefully.

Picture someone who is "bent with care" or "dragging with fatigue." These expressions suggest someone whose movements are slow and heavy. Ideally, your standing and sitting posture should be balanced and easy to maintain for long periods of time without undue fatigue.

To achieve this state it is necessary to continue to practice the art of true relaxation by focusing your attention at the "one point." By doing so you relax spontaneously, the weight of every part of your body will naturally be at its lowest point and you will experience a state of calmness and strength.

4. *Extend Ki.*
As we have seen in the preceding chapters, the Ki generated through your mind and body is constantly interchanging with the universal Ki. Just as electricity is composed of a positive and a negative element, your personal Ki energy ebbs and flows with a similar current. When the current is strong, when you are extending Ki, your positive state of mind is reflected in everything that you say and do. As you extend Ki you further strengthen the current and the supply of Ki readily flows back to you, providing the basis for living a happy, vigorous, and healthy life.

Practicing the Four Basic Principles

Initially if you experience difficulty concentrating on the four principles together, you can still benefit by working with just one at a time. As you practice you will soon discover that by focusing your attention on one principle you will be in alignment with the other three. That is because, although they are different, they each provide a means to the same goal.

By working with principles two and three you are mainly concentrating on the body and by working with principles one and four you are working with the mind. Because both your body and your mind equally respond to the flow of Ki energy, you will feel the results more and more as you continue your practice.

Sources for Additional Information

Acupressure Workshop
1533 Shattuck Ave.
Berkeley, CA 94709
Has a list of local practititioners and gives state-approved training programs in three California locations.

American Center for the Alexander Technique
142 West End Ave.
New York, NY 10023
The center will send you a list of practitioners. (Enclose a self-addressed envelope.)

American Chiropractice Association
1916 Wilson Blvd. Suite 300
Arlington, VA 22201
The Association makes referrals and publishes a newsletter.

American College of Traditional Chinese Medicine
2400 Geary Blvd.
San Francisco, CA 94115
The College has classes in acupuncture, acupressure, and herbology. It maintains a referral list and publishes a quarterly magazine; *Journal of Traditional Chinese Medicine.*

American Osteopathic Association
J212 East Ohio St.
Chicago, IL 60611
They have worldwide referral service.

Center for Chinese Medicine
2303 Garfield Ave. Suite 202
Monterey Park, CA 91753
A source for information concerning acupuncture and acupressure.

Clown Camp and Laugh-Makers Camp
Richard Snowberg, Camp Director
University of Wisconsin La Crosse
1725 State Street
LaCrosse, WI 54601

Feldenkrais Guild
P.O. Box 11145
San Francisco, CA 94101
The Guild has a list of all certified therapists and also will tell you about seminars in your area.

Fun Technicians, Inc. and Laugh Makers
P.O. Box 160
Syracuse, NY 13215
A magazine for everyone. Experienced performers from balloonlogists to chalk talkers share their knowledge and expertise with readers.

Healing Arts Center
17280 Saticoy St.
Van Nuys, CA 91406
Has available certified health therapists and healing classes.

International Institute of Reflexology
Box 12462
St. Petersburg, FL 33733
The Institute can supply you with a list of qualified therapists and seminars in your area.

Laugh Lover's News
Virginia Tooper (The Laugh Professor)
P.O. Box 1495
Pleasanton, CA 94566
Member's receive bi-monthly copies of the Laugh Lover's News.

Laughing Matters
The Humor Project
110 Spring St.
Saratoga Springs, NY 12866
A quarterly magazine devoted to the positive uses of humor.

Mack McGinnis' Favored Quotes
Compiled by Mack McGinnis
448 N. Mitchner Ave.
Indianapolis, IN 43219
Current jokes quotations and topical humor by subscription.

Rolf Institute
P.O. Box 1868
Boulder, CO 80302
They have a worldwide directory.

The Whole Mirth Catalog
1034 Page St.
San Francisco, CA 94117
A catalog filled with items "just for fun."

Suggestions for Future Reading

"Acupuncture: A Curious Cure That Works." *Changing Times* (November 1980), p. 39.

Aihara, Herman. *Basic Macrobiotics*. Tokyo and New York: Japan Publications, Inc., 1985.

American Health Magazine. *The Relaxed Body Book*. Garden City, N.Y.: Doubleday and Co., Inc., 1986.

Anderson, Bob. *Stretching*. Bolinas, Calif.: Shelter Publications, 1980.

Bahr, Robert. *Good Hands*. New York: New American Library, 1984.

Baloti, Lawrence. *Massage Techniques*. New York: Putnam Publishing Group, 1985.

Baloti, Lawrence, and Lewis Harrison. *Massageworks*. New York: Putnam Publishing Group, 1983.

Brannan, Cronin and Glenn. *The New American Vegetable Cookbook*. Berkeley, Calif.: Aris Books, 1985.

Brewster, Letitia, and Michael F. Jacobson. *The Changing American Diet*. Washington D. C.: Center for Science in the Public Interest Publishing, 1978.

Brody, Jane. *Jane Brody's Nutrition Book*. New York: Bantam Books, 1981.

Brown, Barbara. *Stress and the Art of Biofeedback*. New York: Bantam Books, 1982.

Brown, Sarah. *The Best of Vegetarian Cuisine*. New York: Random House Inc., 1982.

Chaitow, Leon. *Acupuncture: Treatment of Pain*. New York: Thorstons Publishers, 1984.

Chia, Mantak. *Awaken Healing Energy through the Tao*. New York: Aurota Press, 1983.

———. *Chi Self Massage: The Taoist Way of Rejuvenation*. Huntington, N.Y.: Healing Tao Books, 1986.

———. *Taoist Ways to Transform Stress into Vitality*. Huntington, N.Y.: Healing Tao Press, 1985.

———. *Transform Stress into Vitality*. Huntington, N.Y.: Healing Tao Press, 1985.

Cooper, Kenneth. *The Aerobic Program for Total Well-being*. New York: Bantam Books, 1982.

Corbin, Cheryl. *Nutrition*. New York: Holt, Rinehart & Winston, 1980.

Dardick, Irving. *Quantum Fitness*. New York: Simon and Schuster, 1984.

Dass, Ram. *The Only Dance There Is*. Garden City, N.Y.: Anchor Books, 1974.

Davis, M. *The Relaxation and Stress Workbook*. San Francisco, Calif.: New Harbinger Publishers, 1980.

DeMente, Boyce. *Secrets of Graceful Living*. Phoenix, Ariz.: Phoenix, Books Publishers, 1982.

Deutsch, Ronald, M. *Realities of Nutrition*. Calif.: Bull, Palo Alto, 1976.

Diamond, Harvey. *Fit for Life*. New York: Warner Books, 1985.

Diamond, John, M.D. *Life Energy*. New York: Dodd, Mead & Co., 1985.

———. *Your Body Doesn't Lie*. New York: Warner Books, 1983.

Diamond, Marilyn. *The Common Sense Guide to a New Way of Eating*. Santa Monica, Calif.: Golden Glow Publishers, 1979.

Dombrowski, Daniel. *The Philosophy of Vegetarianism*. Amherst, Mass.: University of Massachusetts Press, 1984.

DuBelle, Lee. *Proper Food Combining*. Phoenix, Ariz.: Du-Two Publishing, 1985.

Durckheim, Karlfried. *Hara: The Vital Center of Man*. London: George Allen and Unwin Ltd., 1962.

Echols, Barbara. *Vegetarian Delights*. Woodbury, N.Y.: Barron's Educational Series, 1981.

Eisenberg, David. *Encounters with Qi*. New York: W. W. Norton, 1985.

Eliot, Rose. *Vegetarian Dishes from around the World*. New York: Pantheon Books, 1982.

Esko, Edward and Wendy. *Macrobiotic Cooking for Everyone*. Tokyo and New York: Japan Publications, Inc., 1980.

Esko, Wendy. *Aveline Kushi's Introducing Macrobiotic Cooking*. Tokyo and New York: Japan Publications, Inc., 1987.

Farquhar, John W., M.D. *The American Way of Life Need Not Be Hazardous to Your Health*. New York: Norton, 1978.

Fedenkrais, Moshe. *Awareness through Movement*. New York: Harper and Row, Publishers, Inc., 1972.

Fixx, Jim. *The Second Book of Running*. New York: Random House, 1981.

Halpern, Steven. *Sound Health*. San Francisco, Calif.: Harper and Row, 1985.

Hamilton, Eva May, and Eleanor Noss Whitney. *Nutrition: Concepts and Controversies*. St. Paul, Mo.: West Publishers, 1979.

Hartbarger, Janie and Neil. *Eating for the Eighties*. Philadelphia, Pa.: Saunders Press, 1981.

Hass, Elson. *Staying Healthy with the Seasons*. Berkeley, Calif.: Celestial Arts, 1981.

Heisei, Dorelle. *The Biofeedback Guide*. New York: Gordon and Breach Science Publishers, 1977.

Ineson, John. *The Way of Life: Macrobiotics and the Spirit of Christianity*. Tokyo and New York: Japan Publications, Inc., 1986.

Kaptchuk, Ted. *The Web That Has No Weaver: Understanding Chinese Medicine*. New York: Congdon and Weed, 1983.

Kendig, Joan and Keith. *Modern Vegetable Protein Cookery*. New York: Arco Publishing Inc., 1980.

Kirshman, John D., and Lavon Dune. *Nutrition Almanac*. New York: McGraw-Hill Book Co., 1984.

Knocking at the Gate of Life. Translated by Edward Chang. Emmaus, Pa.: Rodale Press, 1985.

Kotzsch, Ronald. *Macrobiotics: Yesterday and Today*. Tokyo and New York: Japan Publications, Inc., 1985.

Kravette, Steve. *Complete Meditation*. Glouster, Mass.: Para Research, 1982.

Kushi, Aveline, and Wendy Esko. *The Changing Seasons Macrobiotic Cooking*. Wayne, N. J.: Avery Publishing Group, 1983.

———. *Macrobiotic Family Favorite: Cooking for Healthy Children*. Tokyo and New York: Japan Publications, Inc., 1986.

Kushi, Michio. *The Book of Dō-In: Exercise for Physical and Spiritual Development*. Tokyo and New York: Japan Publications, Inc., 1979.

———. *The Book of Macrobiotics: The Universal Way of Health, Happiness and Peace*. Tokyo and New York: Japan Publications, Inc., 1986 (Rev. ed.).

———. *How to See Your Health: The Book of Oriental Diagnosis*. Tokyo and New York: Japan Publications, Inc., 1980.

———. *Natural Healing through Macrobiotics*. Tokyo and New York: Japan Publications, Inc., 1978.

Kushi, Michio, and Alex Jack. *Diet for a Strong Heart*. New York: St. Martin's Press, 1984.

Kushi, Michio and Aveline. *The Macrotiotic Diet*. Tokyo and New York: Japan Publications, Inc., 1985.

Kushi, Michio, with Marc Van Cauwenberghe. *Macrobiotic Home Remedies*. Tokyo and New York: Japan Publications, Inc., 1985.

Kushi, Michio, with Stephen Blanuer. *The Macrobiotic Way*. Wayne, N. J.: Avery Publishing Group, 1985.

Leboyer, Frederick. *The Art of Breathing*. Longmead, England: Element Books Ltd., 1985.

Lewith, George T. *Acupuncture: Its Place in Western Medical Science*. Wellingborough, Northamptonshire, England: Thorstons Publishers Ltd., 1980.

————. *Acupuncture: Treatment of Internal Disease*. London: Thorstons Publishing Group, 1985.

Lidell, Lucinda. *The Book of Massage*. New York: Simon and Schuster, 1984.

Loehr, James, and Jeffrey Migdow. *Take a Deep Breath*. New York: Villard Books, 1986.

Maanum, Armand. *Swedish Massage*. Minneapolis, Minn.: Winston Press, Inc., 1985.

Manaka, Yoshio, and Ian A. Urguhart. *Layman's Guide to Acupuncture*. New York: Weatherhill Publishers, 1972.

Marcus, Paul. *Acupuncture: A Patients' Guide*. New York: Thorston's Publishers, Inc., 1985.

Maruyama, Koretoshi. *Aikido with Ki*. Tokyo: Ki no Kenkyukai, 1984.

Masunaga, Shizuto, with Wataru Ohashi and the Shiatsu Center of America. *Zen Shiatsu: How to Harmonize Yin and Yang for Better Health*. Tokyo and New York: Japan Publications, Inc., 1977.

Masunaga, Shizuto, with Stephen Brown. *Zen Imagery Exercises: Meridian Exercises for Wholesome Living*. Tokyo and New York: Japan Publications, Inc., 1987.

Mayer, Jean. *A Diet for Living*. New York: Pocket Books, 1975.

Millman, Dan. *The Warrior Athlete*. Walpole, N. H.: Stillpoint Publishing Co., 1979.

Miyamoto Musashi. *A Book of Five Rings*. Translated by Victor Hartarger. Woodstock, N. Y.: Overlook Press, 1974.

Moore, Kathleen. *The Vegetarian Times Guide to Dining in the USA*. New York: Vegetarian Times Editors, 1980.

Nakamura, Takashi. *Oriental Breathing Therapy*. Tokyo and New York: Japan Publications, Inc., 1981.

Namikoshi, Toru. *The Complete Book of Shiatsu Therapy*. Tokyo and New York: Japan Publications, Inc., 1981.

————. *Shiatsu+Stretching*. Tokyo and New York: Japan Publications, Inc., 1985.

Ni, Daoshing. *Crane-Style Qigong*. Los Angeles, Calif.: Union of Tao and Mann Press, 1986.

Null, Gary. *The Food Combining Handbook*. New York: Berkeley Publishing Group, 1983.

Olinekova, Gayle. *Go for It*. New York: Simon and Schuster, 1982.

Parsley, Sally. *The Tao of Cooking*. Berkeley, Calif.: Ten Speed Press, 1982.

Rama, Swami, Ballentine, Rudolph, M.D., Hymes, Alan, M.D. *The Science of Breath: A Practical Guide*. Pa.: The Himalayan International Institute of Yoga Science and Philosophy, 1981.

Reed, William. *Ki: A Practical Guide for Westerners*. Tokyo and New York: Japan Publications, Inc., 1986.

Robertson, Laurel. *Laurel's Kitchen*. Petaluma, Calif.: Nilgiri Press, 1985.

Rohe, Fred. *The Zen of Running*. New York: Random House, 1975.

Sabry, Zak, and Ruth Fremes. *Nutriscore*. New York: Methuen/Two Continents, 1976.

Saotome, Mitsugi. *Aikido and the Harmony of Nature*. London: Hastings Publications, 1984.

Selye, Hans. *Stress without Distress*. New York: New American Library, 1974.

Sergel, David. *The Macrobiotic Way of Zen Shiatsu*. Tokyo and New York: Japan Publications, Inc., 1989.

Serizawa, Katsusuke, M.D. *Effective Tsubo Therapy: Simple and Natural Relief without Drugs*. Tokyo and New York: Japan Publications, Inc., 1984.

———. *Tsubo: Vital Points for Oriental Therapy*. Tokyo and New York: Japan Publications, Inc., 1976.

Serizawa, Katsusuke, M.D., with Mari Kusumi. *Clinical Acupuncture: A Practical Japanese Approach*. Tokyo and New York: Japan Publications, Inc., 1988.

Shalin, Judith, M.D. *The Romantic Vegetarian*. Chicago: Chicago Review Press, 1983.

Sheldon, Herbert M. *Food Combining Made Easy*. San Antonio, Tex.: Willow Publishing, Inc., 1984.

Shulman, Martha Rose. *The Vegetarian Feast*. New York: Harper and Row, Publishers, Inc., 1979.

Sivanda Yoga Center. *Yoga*. New York: Simon and Schuster, 1985.

Sokie-an. *Twenty-five Koans*. New York: First Zen Institute of America, 1947.

Spreads, Carola H. *Ways to Better Breathing*. Great Neck, N.Y.: Felix Morrow, Publishers, 1986.

Steinbrecher, Edwin. *The Inner Guide Meditation*. Wellingborough, Northhamptonshire, England: Aquarian Press, 1978.

Stevens, John. *The Sword of No Sword (Aikido)*. Boulder, Colo.: Shambala Publications, 1984.

Stevens, John, and Shirata Rinjiro. *Aikido: The Way of Harmony*. Boulder, Colo.: Shambala Publications, 1984.

Stoddard, Allen. *Osteopathic Technique*. New York: Humanities Press, 1979.

Sunset International Vegetarian Cookbook. Menlo Park, Calif.: Lane Publishing, Co., 1983.

Sunset Vegetarian Cooking. Menlo Park, Calif.: Lane Publishing Co., 1985.

Szilard and Woo. *The Electric Vegetarian: Natural Cooking the Food Processor Way*. Boulder, Colo.: Johnson Publishing Co., 1980.

Takahashi, Masaru, and Stephen Brown. *Qigong for Health: Chinese Traditional Exercise for Cure and Prevention*. Tokyo and New York: Japan Publications, Inc., 1986.

Tara, William. *Macrobiotics and Human Behavior*. Tokyo and New York: Japan Publications, Inc., 1984.

Tegner, Bruce. *Kung Fu and T'ai Chi*. Ventura, Calif.: Thor Publishing Co., 1981.

Tohei, Koichi. *Book of Ki: Co-ordinating Mind and Body in Daily Life*. Tokyo and New York: Japan Publications, Inc., 1979.

———. *Ki in Daily Life*. Tokyo: Ki no Kenkyukai, 1978.

Tracy, Lisa. *The Gradual Vegetarian*. New York: Evans and Co., 1985.

Ueshiba, Kisshomaru. *Aikido*. Tokyo: Hozansha, 1985.

Ullyot, Joan. *Running Free*. New York: Putnam and Sons, 1980.

Van Lysebeth, Anddre. *Pranayama: The Yoga of Breathing*. Boston and London: Unwin Paperbacks, 1979.

Waitz, Grete. *Conquer Stress*. New York: Van Nostrans Reinhold Co., 1983.

Wensel, Luise O. *Acupuncture for Americans*. Reston, Va.: Reston Publishing Co., 1980.

White, James R. *Jumo for Joy*. New York: Arco Publishing Co., 1983.

Wile, Douglas. *T'ai Chi Touchstones*. Brooklyn, N.Y.: Sweet Chi Press, 1983.

Wurtman, Judith J. *Eating Your Way through Life*. New York: Raven Press, 1979.

The Yellow Emperor's Classic of Internal Medicine. Translated by Ilza Veith. Berkeley, Calif.: University of California Press, 1949.

Zhou, Dahong, M.D. *The Chinese Exercise Book*. Pt. Roberts, Washington: Hartley and Marks, Ltd., 1984.

Zucker, Judi. *How to Eat without Meat Naturally*. Santa Barbara, Calif.: Woodbridge Press Publishing Co., 1981.

Miscellaneous

Dietary Goals for the United States. Prepared by the Senate Select Committee on Nutrition and Human Needs, sold under Stock No. 05–070–04376–8 by the Superintendent of Documents, U.S. Government Printing Office, Washington, D.C. 20402

Food. A full-color, 64-page magazine, including a daily food guide and recipes, published by the U.S. Department of Agriculture in 1979. Single free copies (order no. G-228) can be obtained from the Consumer Information Center, Department 693-G, Pueblo, Colorado 81009. Copies are also for sale (Stock No. 001–000–03881–8) from the Superintendent of Documents, U.S. Government Printing Office, Washington, D.C. 20402

Nutrition and Your Health: Dietary Guidelines for Americans. A 20 page pamphlet published in 1980 by the U.S. Department of Agriculture and Health, Education and Welfare. Available free from the Office of Governmental and Public Affairs, U.S. Department of Agriculture, Washington, D.C. 20250

The Prudent Diet. A 32 page booklet available free from the Bureau of Nutrition, New York City Department of Health, 93 Worth Street, Room 714, New York, New York 10013

Bostonia Stress Guide. Boston, Mass. December, 1982

Index